HumanBiology

genetics

Text Authors

H. Craig Heller
Angelo Collins

Activity Authors

Stan Ogren
Angelo Collins
Geraldine Horsma
Marjorie Gray

H. Craig Heller, **Principal Investigator**
Mary L. Kiely, **Project Director**

An Interdisciplinary Life Science Curriculum for the Middle Grades
Developed by the Program in Human Biology at Stanford University

EVERYDAY LEARNING®

Chicago, Illinois

Permissions
The Language of Genes Solving the Mysteries of Our Genetic Past, Present and Future by Steve Jones, Anchor Books, published by Doubleday, 1995.

Photo Credits
1 (top center), D. Young-Wolff/PhotoEdit; 6 (top center), Dr. Dennis Kunkel/Phototake; 9 (top) Drawing from Murray Barr, *Biological Science: A Molecular Approach,* BSCS Blue Version, 4th ed. (Lexington, Mass.: D.C. Heath, 1980), 306; 11 (top center), Claude Revy Jean/Phototake; 20 (top center), G. Shih-R. Kessel/Visuals Unlimited; 27 (top center), LLNL/Science Source/Photo Researchers, Inc.; 31 (top center), UPI/Corbis-Bettmann; 41 (top center), Stan Flegler/Visuals Unlimited; 42 (top left), Jim Stevenson/Science Photo Library/Photo Researchers, Inc.; 47 (top center), Michael Newman/PhotoEdit; 51 (top center), Associated Press

Cover Image
Tony Stone Images/DNA strands interlocking to create meshwork

Everyday Learning Development Staff
Editorial
Steve Mico
Leslie Morrison
Susan Zeitner

Production/Design
Fran Brown
Annette Davis
Jess Schaal
Norma Underwood

Additional Credits
Project Editor: Dennis McKee

Shepherd, Inc.

ISBN 1-57039-685-X

Stanford University's Middle Grades Life Science Curriculum Project was supported by grants from the National Science Foundation, Carnegie Corporation of New York, and The David and Lucile Packard Foundation. The content of the Human Biology curriculum is the sole responsibility of Stanford University's Middle Grades Life Science Curriculum Project and does not necessarily reflect the views or opinions of the National Science Foundation, Carnegie Corporation of New York, or The David and Lucile Packard Foundation.

Any questions regarding this policy should be addressed to:
Everyday Learning Corporation
P.O. Box 812960
Chicago, IL 60681

1 2 3 4 5 6 7 8 9 VL 03 02 01 00 99 98

Contents

1

Continuity and Diversity

What makes one species different from another?

Look around your classroom and notice how much you and your classmates look alike. Each of you has a head, arms, legs, eyes, ears, a nose, hair, fingers, toes, and so on. Your classmates are all human beings. You could easily make a list of characteristics that most human beings have in common. **Characteristics** are distinctive qualities of living things. In this unit you will explore what determines different characteristics of living organisms and how characteristics are passed from generation to generation.

To study living things, both plants and animals, we sort them into groups that have similar characteristics. Think about your pets, for example. All cats have similar characteristics. You are able to recognize a cat when you see one. You could make a list of the characteristics of cats that set cats apart from other animals. Even though cats and dogs both have two ears and a tail, you probably don't confuse a cat with a dog. Dogs have characteristics that make them different from cats. What are some of the characteristics that help distinguish cats from dogs?

Figure 1.1 Cats and dogs have many similarities, but the differences in characteristics show that one is a cat and one is a dog.

MINI ACTIVITY

Peanut Sort
Select a peanut from a bag of peanuts with their shells. Write a description of your peanut. You may want to weigh or measure it to make the description more detailed. Please do not mark your peanut. Now mix your peanut with 5 or 10 other peanuts. Can you find your peanut? Explain how you can distinguish your peanut from the rest. Now mix your peanut with a whole bowl of peanuts. Can you still distinguish your peanut from the rest? Describe how.

MINI ACTIVITY

Human Variations
Traits are what make us human. Scientists who study heredity use the term **trait** to speak about characteristics that can be passed from generation to generation. Traits are common to all members of a species. In fact, traits are the characteristics that define a species. Observe your classmates again. This time, record how they are similar. Observe variations (differences) and record your observations. Review all of your observations. List those traits that are unique to human beings and, therefore, distinguish us from other species. List those traits that are shared with other kinds of animals.

Plants also have characteristics that can be used to sort them into groups. You do not confuse oak trees and maple trees, even though both are trees. You can tell the difference between tulips and daffodils because they have different characteristics.

One characteristic of living things that belong to the same group is that they can reproduce to produce offspring that have characteristics similar to those of the parents. For example, when cats reproduce, they have kittens. Dogs produce puppies, and horses produce foals. And two human beings reproduce a human baby, not a puppy.

The same phenomenon—like produces like—is true of plants, as well as animals. For example, a farmer's corn seeds produce corn. An acorn that is planted by a forest ranger will grow into a new oak tree that will produce more acorns. If you plant marigold seeds in your garden you expect more marigolds. These marigolds will in turn produce more marigold seeds.

A group of living things that has similar characteristics and can interbreed (reproduce among themselves) is called a **species.** The phenomenon of living things producing offspring with similar characteristics is **continuity.**

Look at your classmates again. They are all the same species. You are all members of the species *Homo sapiens.* Now take another good look around at your classmates. Though you are all the same species, you are different from one another in many ways. Some classmates have blond hair. Some have black hair. There are probably many shades of brown hair among your classmates, too. Some have straight hair, while others have hair that is wavy or curly. Some classmates are probably taller than others are. Some are male and others are female. Some have dark skin while others have fair skin. Some have noses that are long and thin, while others have short, turned-up noses. Just as you have no difficulty distinguishing human beings from other groups of living things, you have no difficulty distinguishing individual human beings from one another. Even if there is a set of identical twins in your class, you probably can tell them apart.

It is possible to distinguish individuals belonging to the same species of all living organisms. If you have ever selected a new puppy from a litter, you know that each puppy is different, and you know that it is possible to tell the puppies apart. If you have chosen a pet parakeet from a cage with four or five parakeets, you knew which one you wanted—just any parakeet probably would not do. If you look carefully at a row of tulip plants, you will be able to describe each individual plant. Some have broader leaves than others do. Some have red petals, while others have petals that are pink.

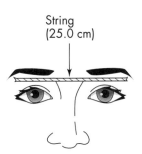

String
(25.0 cm)

Figure 1.2 Eye width.

Did You Know?
Genes are regions of DNA that control traits and carry the trait from one generation to the next generation.

M I N I   A C T I V I T Y

Eye Variation
To measure eye width, you need to work with a partner. You need a ruler (metric) and a piece of string about 25 cm long. While one partner closes his or her eyes, the other partner measures the eye width from the outside corner of one eye across the bridge of the nose to the outside corner of the other eye. Mark the string by holding it with the thumb and forefinger of each hand at the outside corners of each eye. While holding the string, move it to the table. Line up the string along a ruler and measure the length of the string. This is the eye width. Record the measurements on a class chart. Now reverse roles with your partner.

The difference among living organisms is called **diversity.** Diversity exists even among living organisms within the same species.

Genetics is the study of the biological causes of continuity and diversity among living things. Geneticists are scientists who study genetics. They study the biological causes for the similarities and differences between members of the same species. Remember that the word trait means a characteristic that all members of the same species have and is the same. Geneticists use the word **variation** when they mean the characteristics that make members of the same species different from one another. Variations are the different forms of a trait. For humans, having hair is a trait, but the many colors of hair are variations of that trait. Your set of variations makes you special. There is no one else in the world exactly like you. Even if you have a twin, there are differences between you and your twin.

Geneticists are interested in the biological causes of continuity and diversity. They are concerned with traits and variations that are inherited. Inherited characteristics are characteristics that can be passed from parents to their offspring (from one generation to the next). For example, a geneticist would not study human hair length, since humans style their hair differently, which often includes cutting hair. Hair length is not inherited in humans. A geneticist might be interested in hair color, but would have to make sure the hair color was natural and not dyed.

apply your KNOWLEDGE

Identify each of the following as either a trait or a variation.

a. Parrot has feathers.

b. Cat has a striped coat.

c. Geranium plant has flowers.

d. Jasmine has two arms.

e. Dog has droopy ears.

f. Rosebush has thorns.

g. Jamie has freckles.

Activity 1-1
Fingerprinting

Introduction

What is your unique fingerprint pattern? One way to tell the difference between human beings is to look at their fingerprints. Even the fingerprints of identical twins are different. However, there are only 4 patterns of fingerprints—the whorl, the loop, the arch, and the composite. One of these patterns is on each finger. If you examine all ten of your fingers, you might find all of the patterns, or you might find only one of the patterns. In this activity you determine the fingerprint pattern of each of your fingers.

Whorl   Loop   Arch   Composite

Figure 1.3 The four patterns of fingerprints.

Materials

Stamp pad
Magnifying glass
Ruler (metric)
Clear tape
Paper towels and soap, or packaged hand wipes
Activity Report

Procedure

Step 1   Look carefully at the four basic finger-print patterns shown in Figure 1.3. Note the differences among the four patterns.

- In the whorl pattern, ridges circle around a point.
- In the loop pattern, ridges enter from one side, form a loop in the center, and exit from the same place.

- In the arch pattern, ridges flow across the finger with a rise in the center.
- In the composite pattern, there is a combination of two or more of the other three patterns.

Step 2   Wash and dry your hands.

Step 3   Have your partner press each of your fingers onto the pad. DO NOT ROLL YOUR FINGER.

Step 4   Have your partner press each finger onto the appropriate section of the chart on your Activity Report. You might want to practice on a plain piece of paper first.

Step 5   Wash your hands before you continue. Protect your fingerprints by covering them with clear tape.

Step 6   Examine each of your fingerprints carefully. You may need the magnifying glass. Decide which of the four patterns is most like yours. Your fingerprints will not look exactly like the patterns in the figure, but should be close enough for you to decide.

Step 7   Write the name of the pattern below each box on your Fingerprint Chart on the Activity Report.

Step 8   Look at the fingerprints of other people in your group and notice how they are the same and how they are different.

Step 9   Enter your prints on a class tally either on the board or on the overhead projector.

MINI ACTIVITY

Continuity and Diversity in Art
Illustrate your knowledge of the terms *continuity, diversity, trait,* and *variation* in a drawing, cartoon, or painting. Make sure your final product reflects your knowledge of the relationships among these terms.

Environment

The external environment plays an important role in shaping (influencing) variations in humans. Sometimes scientists argue which is more important in determining some variations—the genes or the environment. Scientists refer to this argument as the nature versus nurture argument—where nature refers to the genes and nurture to the environment. Both environment and genes play an important part in causing variations. Let's look at an example. The mother's body is the environment for the unborn child, so it is important that a woman takes especially good care of herself before and during her pregnancy. If a woman drinks alcohol when she is pregnant, her baby can be born with abnormal characteristics that are referred to as fetal alcohol syndrome. One of the abnormal characteristics is mental retardation.

MINI ACTIVITY

Wrist Variation
In this activity you measure wrist circumference. To measure the wrist, work with a partner. You need a ruler (metric) and a piece of string about 25 cm long. Have one partner wrap a piece of string once around the other partner's wrist. With the fingers, mark where the string meets. Move the string to the ruler and measure the length of the marked string. This is the wrist circumference. Record the measurement on a class chart and make a graph. Now reverse roles with your partner.

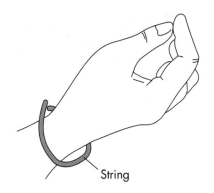

Figure 1.4 Wrist measurement.

 Journal Writing

Describe what everyday life would be like if there were less variety among living things. How would your life be different? What would be the drawbacks to having less diversity, and what are the benefits to having more diversity?

Review Questions

1. What is unique about a species?

2. **a.** What term refers to the phenomenon of living organisms producing offspring with similar characteristics?

   b. What term refers to the phenomenon that all living organisms, even those from the same species, are different from each other?

3. What is the difference between traits and variations?

4. What is genetics? What are geneticists most interested in? Why wouldn't a geneticist be interested in hair length in humans?

2

Cells and Chromo-somes

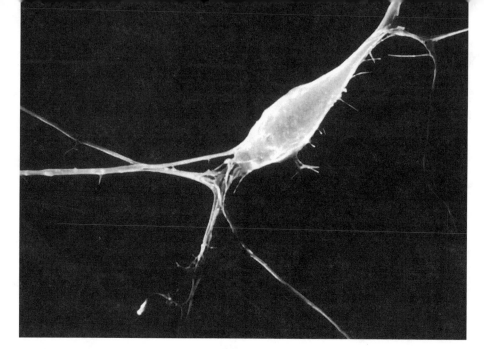

Neuron cell.

How does the individual develop certain characteristics?

We can identify a species by a list of unique traits that are shared by all members of that species but not shared by members of other species. Variations of those same traits also can help us distinguish individuals within the species from one another. Anyone who studies genetics is interested in the biological causes of traits and variations. Geneticists ask questions such as, "Why does Paul have blue eyes when his mother and father both have brown eyes? What color might the kittens be if a black cat and a gray cat reproduced?" Notice that the first question requires an *explanation*. It is a question about something that has happened. The second question requires a *prediction*. It asks about something that may happen or is going to happen. *Geneticists* solve problems that help them *explain* and *predict* the *inheritance* of *traits* and *variations*. (Notice the last sentence had *six words* that were *italicized*. Those six, italicized words have special meaning to scientists. Make sure you know the meanings of all these words!)

"Most of modern genetics is nothing more than a search for variation. Some of the differences can be seen with the naked eye. Others need more sophisticated methods of molecular biology."

—The Language of Genes,
Steve Jones

To solve problems that explain and predict traits and variations, you have to know some things about **cells.** All living organisms are composed of cells. Cells work like little factories doing all the jobs inside your body that are needed to keep your body functioning. Your body is made up of many different kinds of cells such as skin cells, muscle cells, and nerve cells. Some cells look like squashed bricks, some look like doughnuts, and many have irregular shapes. However, every cell, no matter what its job, has the same basic parts.

All human cells have an outer border that is the boundary of the cell. This boundary is called the cell membrane. A liquid material called cytoplasm is inside the cell membrane. There is a large structure suspended in the

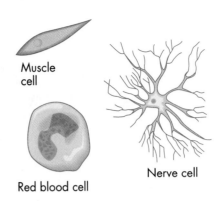

Muscle cell

Red blood cell

Nerve cell

Figure 2.1 Using a microscope, you can tell some cells apart by their appearance. How cells look often tells something about what they do.

Did You Know?

You have 60 trillion cells in your body. While some of your cells will be with you your entire life, other cells have a shorter life span and must make copies of themselves. Many of your body cells make copies of themselves every day, such as red blood cells.

MINI ACTIVITY

Genetics in the News

What is the news in genetics today? Which new discoveries are being made in the areas of genetics in human health? In agriculture, to develop new foods? In productivity of food, to increase quality, improve storage, or quantity? Find a news article related to genetics. Attach the article to a summary sheet on which you have included:

- title;
- source and date;
- summary of contents;
- your opinion of the article, supported by reasons;
- explanation of how this relates to you; and
- what more you would like to know.

Share your information with the class by creating a bulletin board or class resource file.

cytoplasm called the **nucleus.** The nucleus is the part of a cell that contains the genetic information. The nucleus is surrounded by a nuclear membrane that, like the cell membrane, makes a boundary around the nucleus. With few exceptions, every cell in your body has a nucleus. Your mature red blood cells and the cells in the lenses of your eyes do not have nuclei. The cells that give rise to, or produce, your red blood cells and the cells in the lenses have nuclei. However, the mature cells do not.

Inside the nuclear membrane are **chromosomes.** Chromosomes are the cell parts that carry the genes. The genes give us the traits and variations that set us apart as individuals and as a species. Geneticists are constantly trying to learn more about chromosomes and the genes they carry. They study what chromosomes are made of and how they work. Knowing about the structure and function of chromosomes allows us to solve problems about continuity and diversity.

What do we know about chromosomes? We know that chromosomes occur in pairs. We also know that all the individuals of the same species usually have the same number of chromosomes. The chromosomes are located in the nucleus of the cell. The sets of chromosomes in individuals of the same species also look the same in a pair-by-pair comparison. That means that there will be the same number of short pairs and long pairs of chromosomes.

Having the same number and kinds of chromosomes is the reason species have continuity. Chromosome pairs possess information about certain traits, such as hair color, eye color, blood type, the number of fingers and toes, and many other characteristics. Humans have 23 kinds of chromosomes. We have 2 of each kind of chromosome. So humans have a total of 46 chromosomes.

Looking at Chromosomes

How can geneticists see chromosomes? What do they look like? The life cycle of a cell can vary from a few hours to many years depending on the cell. We know that throughout the cell's life chromosomes take on different appearances. Using a microscope you can see chromosomes

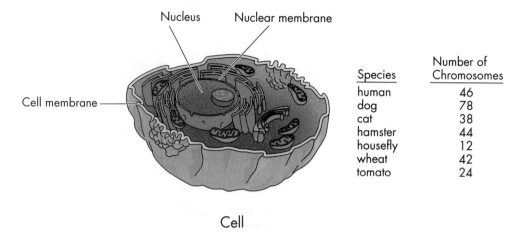

Species	Number of Chromosomes
human	46
dog	78
cat	38
hamster	44
housefly	12
wheat	42
tomato	24

Cell

Figure 2.2 In all species, except very primitive ones such as bacteria, chromosomes are located inside the nucleus of a cell. Although the number of chromosomes may vary between species, the individuals within a species usually have the same number of chromosomes. The number of chromosomes is a trait that distinguishes one species from another.

when a cell is preparing to divide. The chromosomes become compact when they prepare to divide. When this happens within a single chromosome, a point of constriction can be seen. Before the cell divides, the chromosomes replicate. However, the two resulting chromosomes remain attached at the point of constriction. As a result, the replicated chromosome looks like an X.

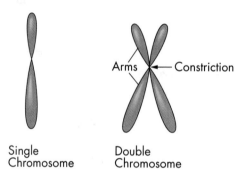

Single Chromosome

Double Chromosome

Figure 2.3 Chromosomes can be distinguished by their arm lengths and by the point where the two chromosome strands meet.

The best way to distinguish one chromosome from another is to stain them. In fact, chromosomes got their name because they can be stained. The word *chromosome* comes from two Greek words meaning color (chroma) and body (soma). Different parts of the chromosome arms absorb dye differently so the chromosomes look like they have horizontal stripes. Chromosomes that are dyed so that they show these stripes are called banded chromosomes.

When we examine chromosomes, we see that the "arms" of different chromosomes are different lengths. Also, the meeting point of the arms is not always in the center. We also can see that the chromosomes can be matched. Notice that each chromosome is double. This process of doubling is called replication. Replication will be discussed later.

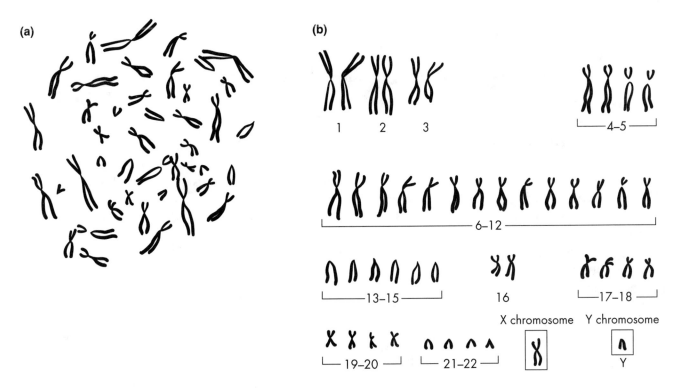

Figure 2.4 (a) All 46 chromosomes in humans are found inside a cell's nucleus. **(b)** To better study chromosomes, scientists have organized and numbered them by size. Karyotypes allow for close study of chromosomes.

A **karyotype** is a portrait of the chromosomes of a cell. Look at Figure 2.4. The first picture (**a**) illustrates all of the chromosomes that are in the nucleus of a human cell. The second picture (**b**) is a karyotype. To make a karyotype, the cell is injected with dye when the chromosome arms are most compact and easy to see. Then the nucleus is squashed so the chromosomes spread out. Next, a photograph is taken through the microscope. Then the individual chromosomes are cut out and arranged. Notice that the chromosomes are paired and ordered from longest to shortest. When chromosomes are the same lengths, they are arranged by the length of the arm. Using this standard arrangement makes it easier to talk about chromosomes because we can identify them by their number.

There is one exception to the rule that chromosomes are paired. While 22 pairs of chromosomes match, the 23rd pair may or may not match each other. This pair of chromosomes makes up the sex chromosomes. If a person has a matched pair of sex chromosomes, the person is a female. Both of the chromosomes look very much like the letter X. If the person has one chromosome that looks like an X and the other that does not look like an X, that person is a male. The chromosome that does not look like an X is called a Y chromosome. Some people think this unpaired chromosome looks like an upside-down letter Y. Females normally have XX chromosomes, and males have XY chromosomes. The sex chromosomes usually are placed last in a karyotype.

In the next section, we'll look more closely at chromosomes and what they are made of.

Activity 2-1
Karyotyping—A Chromosome Portrait

Introduction

What can magnified photographs of your chromosomes tell you? A karyotype is a picture of stained chromosomes arranged in a standard order. Karyotyping is important in diagnosing, learning about, and explaining approximately 100 genetic diseases. The chromosomes are easiest to see when the cells are dividing. In this activity you receive an illustration of chromosomes to cut out and arrange in order on a karyotype sheet. Then you can tell if the chromosomes are from a male or a female. In a karyotype, the chromosomes are paired and ordered from the longest to the shortest. Each duplicated chromosome is held together by a structure known as a centromere. When chromosomes are the same lengths, they are arranged by length of the arm. Each duplicated chromosome is made up of two sister chromatids that are joined together at the centromere. Humans have 22 pairs of matching chromosomes. The 23rd pair of chromosomes may or may not match. This pair of chromosomes is

called the sex chromosomes. Two X chromosomes represent a female (XX), while an X and Y together represent a male (XY). In a karyotype, the sex chromosomes are placed last.

Materials

Scissors
Ruler (metric)
Glue or tape
Resources 1 or 2, and 3
Activity Report

Procedure

Step 1 Using Resource 1 or 2, cut out all the chromosomes.

Step 2 Using Resource 3, arrange the chromosomes in order of size from the longest to the shortest. Glue them in order of size onto Resource 3 (the human karyotype form sheet). Answer the questions on the Activity Report.

 Journal Writing

The person who makes karyotypes is called a cytotechnologist. (Cyto is the Greek word for cell, and technologist comes from the Greek word meaning art.) In Activity 2-1 you did some of the things a cytotechnologist does. Find out what some of the jobs of a cytotechnologist are. Do you think you would want to be a cytotechnologist? If not, why do you think someone else might want to be a cytotechnologist? In a paragraph, explain why or why not you might want to be a cytotechnologist.

 Review Questions

1. Explain three facts that scientists know about chromosomes.

2. Chromosomes exist in pairs with one exception. Describe that exception.

3. What is a karyotype? How is it made? How is a karyotype useful in the study of genetics?

3

Chromo- somes and DNA

Geneticist working on the Human Genome Project.

What is the composition of a chromosome?

Karyotyping was not introduced until the 1950s. However, as early as the 1920s, scientists agreed that chromosomes were made of two chemical substances—**deoxyribonucleic acid (DNA)** and protein. After these substances were identified, the next question was, "Which of these two substances carries the genetic information?" By 1952, results of several experiments led scientists to agree that DNA was the substance responsible for the inheritance of traits. In this section you will learn about DNA.

If DNA is responsible for the inheritance of traits, then what is a **gene?** We hear that word, and we read that word often. For example, "She is a good athlete, because it's in her genes." "A test showed he carries a gene for cystic fibrosis." "Fourteen percent of African Americans carry the gene for sickle-cell anemia." "A gene for pest resistance was inserted into a new variety of potatoes."

A gene is a segment or a region of DNA that codes for a specific trait. What a gene really codes for, however, is a specific protein molecule, and protein molecules are the basis for traits. The questions you now have to ask are, "How does the sequence of DNA code for a protein molecule, and how is the DNA code replicated from cell to cell and organism to organism, so they all have the ability to make specific proteins?" We'll answer the second question first. We'll answer it by learning more about DNA. It's very important to keep in mind that a chromosome is a long DNA molecule, and that the individual segments of that molecule are genes. Each gene is a DNA code that carries information for duplicating itself and for producing a protein molecule.

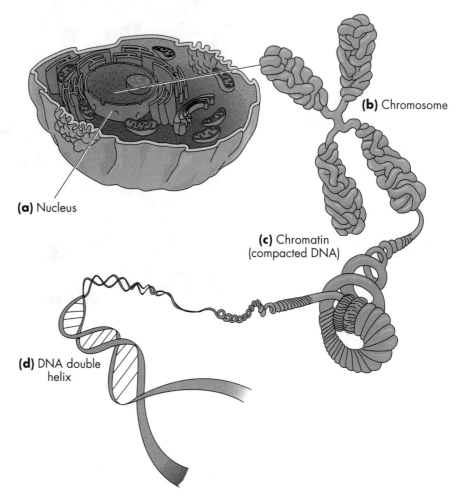

(b) Chromosome

(c) Chromatin (compacted DNA)

(a) Nucleus

(d) DNA double helix

Figure 3.1 (a) Chromosomes are found in the nucleus of a cell. **(b)** Before cells divide, chromosomes duplicate themselves and become compact. The duplicated chromosomes remain together, thus appearing like an X. **(c)** Each chromosome consists of completed coils of DNA called chromatin. **(d)** DNA consists of two strands twisted into a helix.

Did You Know?

Rosalind Franklin was the first person to discover that DNA was in the form of a helix. She and another scientist named Maurice Wilkins used X-rays to investigate the structure of DNA. Watson and Crick later used the X-ray photographs to create their famous model of the DNA structure. Unfortunately, Rosalind Franklin did not share in the 1962 Nobel Prize with the other scientists because she died in 1958. The Nobel Prize is awarded only to living individuals.

In 1953, James D. Watson and Francis H. C. Crick, based on information about DNA from several different scientists, constructed a model of a DNA that explained what was known about DNA at the time. The construction of the model of the *DNA molecule* is considered to be one of the most important events in the history of biology. It allowed scientists to ask even more questions about how genes cause traits and variations. Despite the fact that the construction of this model is so important to genetics, it is interesting to note that Watson and Crick made their first successful model using pieces of cardboard. Later they made a more permanent tin model. Since that time, models of DNA have been made of almost every material imaginable, from glass to gum drops.

apply your KNOWLEDGE

Why do we use models of structures, such as a model of DNA, in science?

Activity 3-1

Precipitation and Spooling of DNA

Introduction

Deoxyribonucleic acid (DNA) is a long molecule that contains the genetic information for gene expression and for the continuity between generations. It is one of the important molecules required for life. What does DNA look like? What are some of its many unique properties? In this activity you have the opportunity to precipitate and spool DNA onto a rod. The DNA has been isolated from the nuclei of cells.

Materials

1 test tube containing 2 ml DNA in solution
4 ml (milliliter) of alcohol
1 50 ml beaker containing strong salt (NaCl) solution and an eyedropper
1 wooden skewer
Activity Report

Procedure

Step 1 Obtain a test tube containing the 2 ml (milliliter) sample of DNA. Examine the solution of DNA. Describe its appearance, color, and viscosity.

Step 2 Use the eyedropper to add 4 or 5 drops of the salt solution to the test tube containing the DNA. Carefully hold the test tube in one hand and tap *gently* on the bottom of the tube to mix.

Step 3 Pour 4 ml of alcohol into the test tube by slowly trickling the entire contents of ethyl alcohol down the side of the test tube containing the DNA and the NaCl.

Step 4 Observe the interface between the two solutions. **Do not mix the two layers.**

Step 5 Place the wooden skewer all the way to the bottom of the test tube that contains the two-layered solution.

Step 6 Observe the interface as you rotate the skewer and wind (spool) the DNA that comes out of the solution onto the skewer. This is not a single DNA molecule, but thousands of molecules. If you have a partner, be sure to take turns spooling.

Step 7 Examine and touch the DNA on the skewer. Record the appearance, color, and texture of the DNA.

Step 8 When you are finished, ask your teacher what to do with your **spooled DNA** and supplies.

What is so special about DNA? What does it do and how does it work? DNA does two important things.

1. It *stores* and *replicates* genetic information.
2. It provides information for *gene expression* through protein synthesis.

Proteins are responsible for cell structure and are the products of gene expression.

 Journal Writing

DNA is frequently the subject of scientific study, and sometimes it is a point of controversy. Watch your local newspapers and select articles about chromosomes and DNA. Write a one-paragraph summary and one paragraph about your opinion and thoughts.

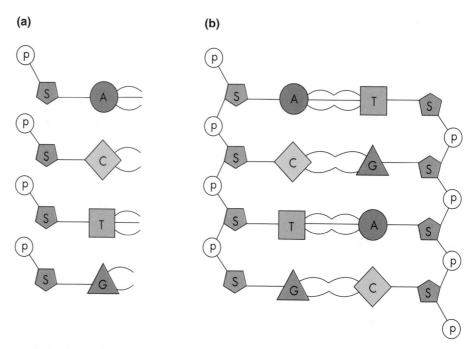

Figure 3.2 (a) Nucleotides consist of a sugar molecule, a phosphate molecule, and one of four nitrogen molecules. **(b)** The four nucleotides fit together like a lock and key, with guanine pairing with cytosine, and adenine pairing with thymine.

Remember that DNA is part of the chromosomes and is located in the nucleus of the cell. The structure of a DNA molecule is simple to learn. A DNA molecule is made up of four different, complex chemical molecules, called **nucleotides.** Each nucleotide is composed of a sugar molecule called deoxyribose, a phosphate molecule, and one of four nitrogen molecules (adenine, guanine, cyostine, and thymine). (See Figure 3.2.)

- A phosphate, a sugar, and an adenine molecule make up the adenine nucleotide.
- A phosphate, a sugar, and a thymine molecule make up a thymine nucleotide.
- A phosphate, a sugar, and a guanine molecule make up the guanine nucleotide.
- A phosphate, a sugar, and a cytosine molecule make up a cytosine nucleotide.

Nucleotides are joined together, one after the other, and form a helix chain. Two of these chains pair. When they pair, they then twist to form a **double helix** (Figure 3.3), which is a name that scientists use meaning two-chained coil or spring.

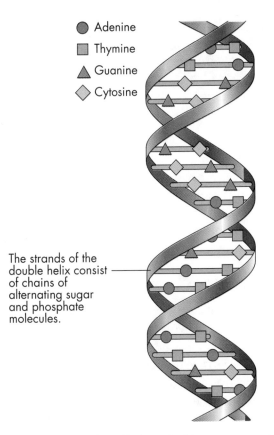

- Adenine
- Thymine
- Guanine
- Cytosine

The strands of the double helix consist of chains of alternating sugar and phosphate molecules.

Figure 3.3 DNA looks like a twisting ladder, with the nucleotides as rungs, and the sugar and phosphate molecules making up the legs (uprights) of the ladder.

What Do You Think?

Science is partly a process of answering questions that produce more questions. What questions come to your mind from the discovery of DNA and its structure?

The structure of DNA is like a twisted ladder. The sugar and phosphates make up the uprights of the ladder. The rungs are made up of pairs of complimentary nitrogen bases. These pairs fit together like a lock and key fit together. They consist either of adenine joined to thymine or cytosine joined to guanine. Because the four nucleotides of DNA can be arranged in any sequence along the strand of DNA, an unlimited number of different DNA molecules are possible.

Activity 3-2
Removing DNA from Thymus Cells

Introduction

What does DNA look like? Where is it found in the cell? How can DNA be removed from a cell so we can see it?

In this activity you answer these questions by treating cells so you can remove DNA. You use thymus cells from an animal whose thymus cells are similar to human thymus cells.

Materials

Sample of fresh thymus cells in beaker
Tap water in beaker
Sand
Liquid soap, clear
Alcohol
Cheesecloth square (several layers, 15 × 15 cm)
Mortar and pestle
Test tube
Small funnel
Test tube rack
Wooden skewer

Forceps
Eyedropper
Permanent marking pen
Paper towels
Black construction paper, 4 × 4 cm
Transparent tape
Microscope, slides, and cover slips
Safety goggles
Activity Report

Procedure

Step 1 Obtain supplies for your team and arrange them at your lab station.

Step 2 Using forceps, place a sample of thymus tissue in the mortar (bowl). Add a pinch of sand and 1 to 2 dropperfuls of water. Use the pestle to grind the thymus well, adding a little more water as necessary to make a thick, souplike mixture. Answer question 1 on your Activity Report.

Step 3 Put a test tube into a test tube rack and place a small funnel in the test tube. Spread a cheesecloth square over the large opening at the top of the funnel.

Step 4 Carefully pour the thymus contents of your mortar in the cheesecloth square and allow the liquid to filter through the cheesecloth and funnel. Carefully draw together the edges of the cheesecloth and use the forceps to help squeeze the remaining liquid from the thymus mixture. Now discard the cheesecloth and its contents into a special waste container as indicated by your teacher.

Step 5 Take a drop of the thymus cell liquid from the test tube. Place it on a microscope slide, and put a cover slip carefully on top of the drop. Observe the slide under a microscope. Then, on your Activity Report, draw what you see. Add labels, if possible. Answer question 2.

Step 6 Add 3 to 4 drops of liquid soap to the liquid in your test tube. Carefully hold the test tube in one hand and gently tap on the bottom of the tube to mix. Answer question 3 on your Activity Report.

Step 7 Mark the level of the liquid in the test tube with a permanent marker.

Step 8 Tilt the test tube and slowly trickle an equal volume of alcohol down the inside of the test tube. Wait 30–60 seconds and carefully observe to see what happens at the interface (where the alcohol and thymus mixtures meet). Answer question 4 on your Activity Report.

Step 9 Place a wooden skewer in the test tube and twirl it. Carefully observe what happens as you twirl the skewer. Keep twirling the skewer until there is no further change. Answer question 5 on your Activity Report.

Step 10 Remove the skewer. Place the skewer on a paper towel and carefully blot it dry. Observe the DNA. What does it look like? How does it feel when you touch it? Record your observations on your Activity Report.

Step 11 Using clean, dry forceps, carefully remove the DNA from the skewer. Place the DNA on a small piece of black construction paper. Use clear tape to cover your specimen to keep it from drying out and to fasten the specimen onto the construction paper. Attach the paper to your Activity Report in the space provided. Complete question 6 on your Activity Report.

Step 12 Wash and dry all the glassware you used during the investigation. Store the materials appropriately.

Activity 3-2 (continued)
Removing DNA from Thymus Cells

Step 13 Design an alternative procedure you could use to explore different ways of removing thymus DNA. One example might be using different soaps. Another procedure might be using different types of alcohol. Record your ideas on the Activity Report. Share your experimental design with your class. Answer question 7 on the Activity Report.

Step 14 How would you modify your experimental design to use different sources for DNA? Which sources would you choose and why? Record your proposals on the Activity Report. Answer question 8.

Did You Know?

All organisms have chromosomes that contain DNA. If all organisms contain DNA, what makes a tulip a tulip and not a dog? What makes a goldfish a goldfish and not a human? The DNA in various species differs in the number and arrangement of the four nucleotides—adenine, guanine, cytosine, and thymine. In fact, every organism has a unique sequence (order) of nucleotides making up the DNA.

Did You Know?

If you stretched out the DNA strand in a single cell, it would be about 6 feet long. Every cell in your body carries a complete set of DNA instructions. This is true even though most of the instructions don't affect the functions of that one cell. DNA is so compact that if you put all of the DNA molecules from all of your cells together, they would be about the size of an ice cube. However, uncoiled and stretched out end to end, the DNA strands would stretch to the sun and back many times!

Replication

One of DNA's most important functions is to make a copy of itself. In making copies of itself, DNA can pass from one generation of cells to the next. When a strand of DNA makes an exact copy of itself, the process is called **replication.** Replication or duplication of DNA occurs just before a cell divides. Replication is very important to the study of genetics and how traits and variations are passed along from generation to generation. How does the strand split during replication? The DNA molecule comes apart where the adenine and thymine meet and where the guanine and cytosine meet. The DNA molecule acts like it is unzipping as it begins to replicate. As the DNA is unzipping, spare pieces of nucleotides that are found in the nucleus are matched to the free ends of adenine, guanine, cytosine, and thymine. Thymine **(T)** bonds to adenine **(A).** Cytosine **(C)** bonds to guanine **(G).** Guanine **(G)** bonds to cytosine **(C).** Adenine **(A)** bonds to thymine **(T).** Two new molecules of DNA are formed that are identical to the original DNA molecule.

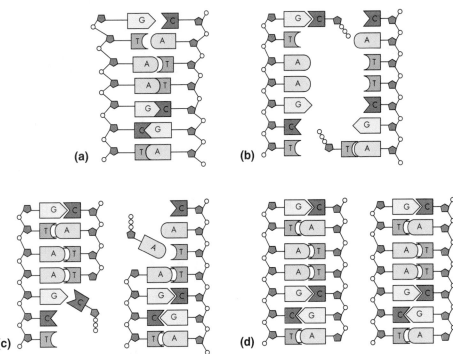

Figure 3.4 (a) When DNA replicates, it unzips. It separates at the point where the nucleotides meet. **(b)** These two strands of DNA **(c)** then pick up extra nucleotides **(d)** until each strand has a complete set of paired nucleotides. The result is two identical strands of DNA.

Section 3 • Chromosomes and DNA

17

Activity 3-3
Building and Using a DNA Model

Introduction
How do nucleotides fit together to make a DNA molecule? What does this double helix molecule look like? In this activity you make a model of DNA. Then you make a copy of your model to learn more about the structure and function of DNA and how it replicates.

Materials
Scissors
6 sets of different colored sheets
Tape
Resource
Activity Report

Procedure
PART A—A DNA MODEL

Step 1   Working in pairs, cut out pieces from the template for each of the following.
A—adenine, red
C—cytosine, yellow
T—thymine, blue
G—guanine, green
P—phosphate, orange
D—deoxyribose (sugar), white

Your task is to make a total of 60 nucleotides:

15 adenine nucleotides containing the nitrogen base adenine;
15 cytosine nucleotides containing the nitrogen base cytosine;
15 thymine nucleotides containing the nitrogen base thymine; and
15 guanine nucleotides containing the nitrogen base guanine.

Make an *adenine nucleotide* by taping together 1 adenine nitrogen base, 1 deoxyribose sugar, and 1 phosphate. Make 14 more adenine nucleotides.

Make 15 *cytosine nucleotides*. Each cytosine nucleotide is made of 1 cytosine, 1 deoxyribose sugar, and 1 phosphate.

Tape the 3 parts of each cytosine nucleotide together.

Make 15 *thymine nucleotides*. Each thymine nucleotide is made of 1 thymine, 1 deoxyribose sugar, and 1 phosphate. Tape the 3 parts of each thymine nucleotide together.

Make 15 *guanine nucleotides*. Each guanine nucleotide is made of 1 guanine, 1 deoxyribose sugar, and 1 phosphate. Tape the 3 parts of each guanine nucleotide together.

Step 2   Build a ladder consisting of 12 nucleotide pairs. Do not use more than 7 individual adenine, guanine, cytosine, or thymine nucleotides that you made. Tape the nucleotides together. Remember that adenine pairs with thymine and cytosine pairs with guanine. Save the remaining nucleotides for Part B of this activity.

Step 3   Hold both ends of the model and gently twist. You have made a "double helix."

Step 4   Answer questions 1 through 5 on the Activity Report.

PART B—REPLICATION

Step 5   Gently untwist your DNA model from Part A and place it in front of you. Separate the 2 halves of your model by cutting between the nitrogen bases (A & T and C & G).

Step 6   Using the extra nucleotides you saved from Part A, add nucleotides to each of the DNA halves. Remember that adenine bonds (connects) with thymine, and cytosine bonds with guanine. Answer questions 6 and 7 on the Activity Report.

Journal Writing

Many people have said that the discovery of DNA is the most important discovery of the 20th century. Do you agree? Why or why not? Find articles from newspapers or magazines about DNA. Use the articles to write your own article that might appear 10 years from now.

Review Questions

1. What is a chromosome made of?

2. What is DNA made of?

3. What is a nucleotide?

4. What is a double helix? What is its structure?

5. Which nucleotide molecules pair together?

6. What happens to DNA during replication?

4

Cell Division

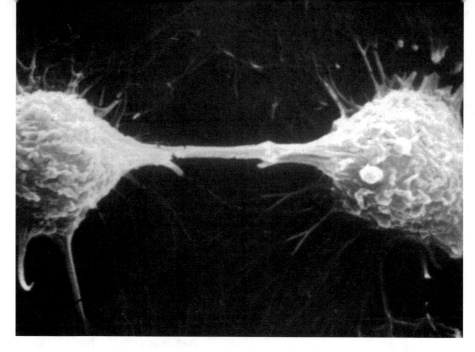

Human cell during mitosis.

How are traits passed from one generation to the next generation?

Remember that one of DNA's most important jobs is to replicate—make a copy of itself. In making copies of itself, DNA can pass from one generation of a family to the next. Genetics is the study of variations that are passed from one generation of a species to another. Before we study why certain variations are passed along in a species, you need to learn how genes are passed along during the reproductive process.

Did You Know?
A cell cycle includes the stages beginning when a cell starts dividing and ending with two new cells. The cell cycle lasts about 18–24 hours. It takes about 6–8 hours for DNA to copy (replicate) itself and about 1 hour for the nucleus and chromosomes to divide. The rest of the time the cell is growing and producing proteins. You will find out about protein synthesis in the next section.

Like sentences make up a paragraph, genes make up chromosomes. Every cell in the human body has a complete set of 46 chromosomes, on which an estimated 100,000 genes are located. Genes are responsible for an individual having the traits he or she has. For example, every human being has a gene for blood type that is located on Chromosome 9. When your body grows by making new cells, and when your body makes new cells to repair an injury, all of the new cells must have 46 chromosomes—your 46 chromosomes specific to you. Every cell has a complete set of chromosomes and genes. When cells divide, the chromosomes also must divide in a very regular way during a process called **mitosis.** Mitosis is the process in which the cell divides, producing two new cells, each with the same number and exact type of chromosomes as the parent cell.

Geneticists know that the traits and variations passed from one generation of a family to another are contained in the chromosomes. They also know that 46 chromosomes must be passed from human parents to their children, so that each new generation has a complete set of chromosomes and genes. Why is this important? It is important

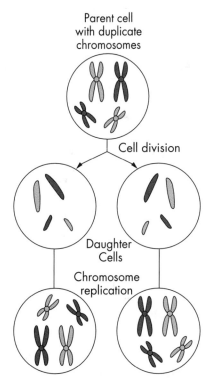

Parent cell
with duplicate
chromosomes

Cell division

Daughter
Cells

Chromosome
replication

Figure 4.1 When a cell divides to produce new cells for the body, the nucleus splits into two, so that each daughter cell gets an identical set of chromosomes. Details of the process are in Activity 4-1.

because genes possess instructions for traits that make us human—instructions for building a person. If instructions are lost, the person may not develop properly. Each pair of chromosomes of an offspring consists of one chromosome from the mother and one chromosome from the father. This happens because gamete cells first go through a different division process called **meiosis.** Meiosis happens before fertilization occurs.

Mitosis

As you learned, mitosis is the process in which the cell divides, producing two new cells. Each of the new cells has the same number and exact type of chromosomes as the parent cell had. Cell division provides for growth or replacement of worn-out cells throughout your body. In mitosis the set of chromosomes divides into two identical sets. Then one cell nucleus becomes two cell nuclei, each containing an identical set of chromosomes. When the cell divides into two, one set of chromosomes goes to each daughter cell so that each new daughter cell has an identical set of chromosomes.

Did You Know?
Not all cells are actively cycling (dividing) at once. Many cells are resting. The lives of cells vary a lot depending on their function. Red blood cells live for about 120 days, while skin cells live only a few days. The nerve cells in your brain last your whole life and do not divide.

Activity 4-1
Cell Division—Double or Nothing

Introduction
Many-celled organisms, including you, begin as a single cell. What is the process of producing millions of cells from a single cell? In this activity you explore how a cell reproduces (divides) to form two new cells. Mitosis is a continuous and orderly process that occurs in your body's somatic cells. In this activity you model each stage of mitosis using pipe cleaners to represent chromosomes.

Materials
Activity Report
Colored crayons or colored pens or pencils (same colors as pipe cleaners if possible)
2 large paper plates
8 pipe cleaners (2 long of color A, 2 long of color B, 2 short of color A, and 2 short of color B)

Procedure
Step 1 Gather four pairs of pipe cleaners to represent the chromosomes. Remember that your somatic cells have 23 pairs of chromosomes. In this activity we follow two pairs of chromosomes through the process of mitosis.

Step 2 Arrange your pipe cleaners so each pipe cleaner in the pair is of the same length and color. Twist each pair together by one turn at the midpoint. Each pair of pipe cleaners represents a duplicated chromosome. The two different colors indicate that one chromosome came from the father and one chromosome came from

Activity 4-1 *(continued)*

Cell Division—Double or Nothing

the mother. Duplicate chromosomes are formed through the process of DNA replication, which occurs before mitosis begins.

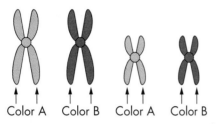

Color A   Color B   Color A   Color B

Figure 4.2 One long and one short pair, color A. One long and one short pair, color B.

Step 3   Take two plates and place one plate on top of the other. The plates represent a cell. Put your chromosomes on the top plate. Using the crayons, draw a picture of the chromosomes on your Activity Report.

This phase (prophase) can be recognized when the double chromosomes are visible and can be observed under the microscope as distinct bodies.

Step 4   Line up the double chromosomes along a line that divides the top plate into two halves. Using crayons or colored pencils, draw a picture of the chromosomes on your Activity Report.

During this phase (metaphase), the chromosomes line up in the middle of the cell.

Step 5   Now separate each double chromosome by untwisting them. Leave them side by side on the midline that runs through the center of the plate. Next, move one single, chromosome of each pair to the left of the

plate and one to the right. Each chromosome is now a single chromosome, and each side of the plate should have two long and two short, single chromosomes.

This phase of mitosis (anaphase) occurs when double chromosomes separate into two single chromosomes that move to opposite sides of the cell.

Step 6   Now it is time for the cell to divide into two daughter cells. You represent this step by bringing out the second plate and moving one set of single chromosomes to it. Each newly formed daughter cell has an identical set of chromosomes—two short and two long chromosomes.

In this phase of mitosis (telophase), the cytoplasm divides, resulting in two daughter cells. Each newly formed daughter cell has a nucleus containing a complete set of chromosomes—two copies of the 23 different chromosomes found in the cell. On your Activity Report, record a colored drawing of the chromosomes placed on each plate.

Step 7   In the next phase (interphase), the chromosomes lose their compact appearance. The chromosomes replicate their DNA so that each single chromosome becomes a duplicated chromosome as you did in Step 2 of the activity.

Step 8   Discuss with your partner the questions on the Activity Report. Then record your responses.

Meiosis

In animals, meiosis produces **gamete cells.** The gamete cells are the cells that are used to reproduce. Meiosis is more complex than mitosis. In meiosis, the chromosomes make copies of themselves as they did in mitosis, but the original cell divides two times. For every cell that begins the process, four new cells are produced. However, the chromosomes have replicated themselves only once. So the four new cells each have half the number of chromosomes of the species. The process of meiosis guarantees that each of these four cells receives one chromosome from each pair of chromosomes. That means that each of these cells has all of the chromosomes and genes that are typical for the species. But each cell has only one copy of each of the chromosomes and genes instead of the two copies that are in all of the other cells of the body. These special cells with half the number of chromosomes are called gamete cells. Gamete cells in males are called **sperm.** Gamete cells in females are called **ova** (eggs). All four cells produced by meiosis in males become sperm. In females, although four cells are produced, only one becomes an **ovum** (singular form of ova, or one egg).

Human gamete cells produced by meiosis have 23 chromosomes. The event of an egg cell or ovum combining with a sperm cell is **fertilization.** In humans when an ovum and sperm join, each cell contributes 23 chromosomes. So the fertilized egg has the normal number of 46 chromosomes—half come from the mother and half come from the father. The fertilized egg is a **zygote.** The zygote goes through round after round of mitosis to produce a fetus, and eventually a baby.

Through meiosis, chromosomes are sorted in a way that separates each pair of chromosomes. Through fertilization, they are recombined into new pairs. This is important for two reasons. First, the number of chromosomes per body cell (46) remains the same from one generation to the next (genetic continuity). Second, because each individual has his or her own unique set of chromosomes, there is greater human variety.

apply your KNOWLEDGE

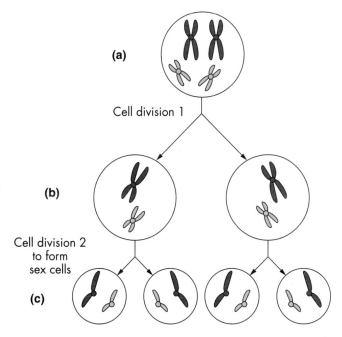

(a)

Cell division 1

(b)

Cell division 2 to form sex cells

(c)

Figure 4.3 Meiosis: **(a)** The first cell has 2 pairs of duplicated chromosomes. **(b)** After the first division, each cell receives one duplicated chromosome from each pair. **(c)** After the second division, each cell receives one copy of each chromosome.

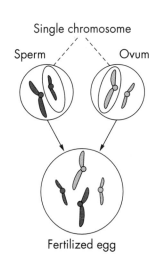

Single chromosome

Sperm   Ovum

Fertilized egg

Figure 4.4 When human sex cells combine to form a fertilized egg, they each bring 23 chromosomes that join to create a new individual. This figure shows 2 of the 23 chromosomes from the father and 2 from the mother.

Activity 4-2
Meiosis and Fertilization

Introduction

What is meiosis? Why is it important? How is it different from mitosis? In this activity you explore how chromosomes sort and recombine through meiosis and fertilization. Meiosis occurs only in the reproductive organs to produce gametes (sperm or eggs).

Materials

Data Sheets 1 and 2
Activity Report
Crayons or colored pens or pencils (same colors as pipe cleaners if possible)
4 large paper plates
4 pairs of pipe cleaners to represent 2 pairs of double chromosomes (2 different lengths and 2 different colors)

Procedure A
Meiosis

Step 1   Work in pairs. In this part of the activity, you model what happens during meiosis. You should work on a flat surface. Remember that you have 23 pairs of chromosomes in each of your somatic cells. In this activity meiosis is simulated using only two pairs of chromosomes. Gather four pairs of pipe cleaners to represent two pairs of double chromosomes. Each chromosome pair is unique. Each contains genes for the same traits. The two pairs of double chromosomes are different from each other in both size and the genetic traits they contain.

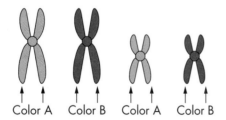

Color A   Color B   Color A   Color B

Figure 4.5 Two pairs of double chromosomes.

Step 2   Stack four plates on top of each other. Place your four double chromosomes *in pairs* on the top plate. The chromosomes are not organized in any particular way. The plate represents the parent cell. Record a colored drawing of the chromosomes on the plate on Data Sheet 1.

Step 3   Now line up the pairs of double chromosomes along a line that divides the plate into two halves. Unlike mitosis, the chromosomes do not line up in a single row. The chromosomes line up in pairs. On Data Sheet 1, record a colored drawing of the chromosomes on the plate.

Step 4   Place one member of each chromosome pair on the left side of the plate. Place the other member of each chromosome pair on the right side of the plate. Each side of the plate should have one long double chromosome and one short double chromosome. On Data Sheet 1, record a colored drawing of the chromosomes on the plate.

Step 5   *Division 1:* Now it is time for the cell to divide for the first time to produce two cells. Carefully separate the stack of four plates so that you have two stacks of two plates each. This is illustrated on Data Sheet 1. Transfer one set of double chromosomes to the other stack of plates. You should have two double chromosomes, each a different size on the top plate of each stack. On Data Sheet 1, record a colored drawing of the chromosomes on the plate.

Step 6 On the top plate of each stack, separate each double chromosome by untwisting the strands. Leave them side by side on the midline through the center of the plate. Next, move one single chromosome of each pair to the left side of the plate and one to the right side of the plate. Each side of the plate should have one long and one short single chromosome. On Data Sheet 1, record a colored drawing of the chromosomes on the plate.

Step 7 ***Division 2:*** Now it is time for the cell to divide again. Position the two stacks so they are about a foot apart. Separate the two plates of each stack so that the two plates of each stack are side by side. This is illustrated on Data Sheet 1. Transfer a set of single chromosomes (one of each kind of chromosome—one short chromosome and one long chromosome) onto the empty plates so that each of the four plates has two single chromosomes. These plates represent the four daughter gamete cells.

Each newly formed daughter cell contains two single chromosomes. On Data Sheet 1, record a colored drawing of the chromosomes on the plate.

Step 8 Discuss with your partner questions 1 and 2 on the Activity Report. Then record your responses to each question.

Procedure B
Fertilization

Step 9 In this part of the activity you model what happens to the chromosomes during fertilization. Work together with another pair of students in the class. Select one of your plates and place it in front of you. Have the other team place one of their plates in front of them. Each plate should have two single chromosomes. The chromosomes on the two plates should be different colors. On Data Sheet 2, record a colored drawing of the chromosomes on the plate.

Step 10 One of the plates represents a sperm cell and the other plate represents an egg cell (ovum). Move the plate representing the sperm cell next to the plate representing the egg cell. Transfer the chromosomes from the plate representing the sperm cell onto the plate representing the egg cell. (Now, there should be four single chromosomes on one of the plates and none on the other.) This process of the union of sperm and egg is called fertilization. The cell with the chromosomes is now called the fertilized egg or zygote. On Data Sheet 2, record a colored drawing of the chromosomes on the plate.

Step 11 Discuss with your group questions 3 through 7 on the Activity Report. Then record your responses.

What is the relationship between DNA replication and the fact that chromosomes are doubled when they begin meiosis?

What Do You Think?

In the models you made of the processes of meiosis and fertilization, you used pipe cleaners in place of chromosomes. You followed only two chromosomes, but imagine how the chromosomes in humans sort and recombine when there are 46 chromosomes. In what other ways were your models of meiosis and fertilization different from the real thing?

You have learned that the genes are segments or regions of DNA and that DNA makes up chromosomes. DNA's job is to preserve a code for cells that tells the cells what to do. Interestingly, genetic codes for different genes can vary a lot. Some are short and others are long. Some have a lot of extra information in them and others do not. Sometimes, this information gets mixed up in the process of replication—resulting in a mutation. A mutation is an error in the order of one or more nucleotides of DNA. These errors can result in well-known diseases, such as those described in Section 7.

Journal Writing

Make a list of the characteristics that make you, you. They can be both characteristics you see, and characteristics in personality or choice of activities. Now separate those characteristics into two groups—those you think you cannot control and are part of your genetic self (nature), and those characteristics you have developed and you think you can change (nurture). How much of who you are is truly genetic, and how much of who you are is a product of how you are raised?

Review Questions

1. What is the difference between mitosis and meiosis?

2. Describe the process of meiosis.

3. Why is meiosis important to the continuity of a species?

4. Why are models important tools for geneticists?

5

Gene Expression— DNA Codes for Proteins

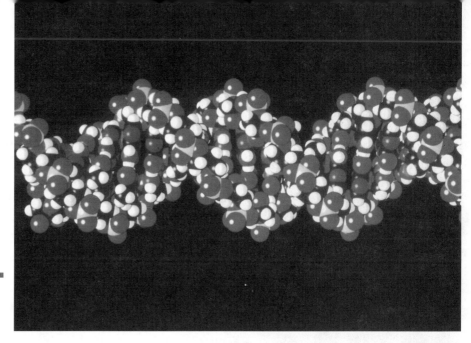

DNA model.

How is information contained in DNA expressed?

DNA has two jobs—one is to replicate and the other is to provide information for making proteins. The process of making proteins is called **protein synthesis.** Protein synthesis is the result of gene expression. And the synthesis of different proteins is what makes us humans.

Proteins are the most complex and diverse of all molecules that make up the human body. Over half of the dry weight of the human body is protein. Protein molecules are very big. Small protein molecules have over 1,000 atoms, while large protein molecules may have over a million atoms. These atoms are organized into molecules called **amino acids.** The amino acids are the building blocks of proteins. A protein can consist of several hundred amino acids. Each species has its own set of proteins. Different cells in your body produce different proteins but have the same DNA.

Proteins do many things in your body. Your muscles are made up of proteins that can contract. Your blood has the protein hemoglobin that carries oxygen to your cells. Your blood has other proteins that cause it to clot. Still other proteins protect you from germs. Proteins, called enzymes, control practically all of the chemical reactions in your cells. The cartilage that forms your joints and gives shape to your ears and nose is a protein. Proteins can do so many different things because they have very different shapes. The specific sequence of amino acids in a protein determines its shape. If a protein loses its shape, it loses its function. When you cook foods, you denature the proteins that are in the plant or animal tissues in the food. Scientists say protein is denatured when it loses its shape.

In other units, you will learn about important protein molecules including hormones, hemoglobin, antibodies, and enzymes. Proteins are very important components of your body and of the bodies of all living things.

A Look at the Information Code

How does a DNA molecule, with only four nucleotides, contain the code for all the different proteins that are found in the human body?

Remember that proteins are made of individual chemical building blocks called amino acids. There are more than 20 different amino acids. Many people have compared amino acids to letters in the alphabet. Just as we put together the letters in the alphabet into different combinations and sequences to make words, the amino acids are put together in different combinations to make different proteins. The DNA molecule contains coded information that controls the order in which the amino acids are put together.

The code in DNA is a three-letter code. How can we read the DNA code? Each sequence of three nucleotides codes for an amino acid. For example, the DNA nucleotide sequence of thymine, cytosine, and adenine (TCA) is a code for the amino acid named serine. Cytosine-adenine-thymine (CAT) is a code for the amino acid named valine. The three nucleotides (triplet) on the DNA molecule that code for an amino acid act as a single unit.

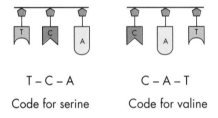

T – C – A   C – A – T

Code for serine   Code for valine

Figure 5.1 The nucleotides thymine, cytosine, and adenine join together to make the code for the amino acid serine. Cytosine, adenine, and thymine make the code for valine. DNA codes for more than 20 amino acids. See the *Did You Know?* about mRNA, in the margin.

The sequence of nucleotides in DNA spells out code words for assembling amino acids to build proteins. These code words can be grouped together like a "sentence" or a message called a gene. The gene tells the cell to use specific amino acids in a specific order to make a particular protein, like hemoglobin.

Putting the Code to Work to Make Protein

DNA is found only in the nucleus, but proteins are produced in the cytoplasm outside the nucleus. So the coded information of DNA must get from the nucleus to the cytoplasm somehow. How is this code of the DNA molecule read to make a protein? Three other molecules are involved in the process for DNA to transmit the code. The three chemicals involved are mRNA, tRNA, and ribosomes. **RNA** is a molecule very much like DNA. It is composed of nucleotides that form base pairs with DNA, but it is a single-stranded molecule rather than a double-stranded helix. Some RNA is in the form of a long chain and travels between the nucleus and the cytoplasm. This RNA called **mRNA** carries the coded message from the DNA in the nucleus to the cytoplasm. The "m" stands for messenger. mRNA is the messenger that takes the DNA code to the

Section 5 • Gene Expression—DNA Codes for Proteins

cytoplasm where proteins are made. There are short pieces of RNA in the cytoplasm that carry or transfer a specific amino acid from the cytoplasm to sites where the proteins are assembled. These sites are called **ribosomes.** Amino acids are joined together to make a protein at the ribosomes. The amino acids are carried (or transferred) to the ribosomes where protein is assembled by RNA called **tRNA.** The "t" stands for transfer. Both mRNA and tRNA are made in the nucleus. Since there are 20 or more amino acids that are used to make proteins, there are more than 20 different tRNAs.

You could think of protein synthesis like a construction project. The ribosomes are the construction sites where the protein is made. The DNA is the architect that has the design for a specific protein. The mRNA is the general contractor. The tRNAs are the various suppliers that bring the raw materials to the construction site, or in this case provide the amino acids for making the protein. The mRNA and the tRNAs meet at the ribosome. The mRNA has the coded message from the DNA, and the tRNAs have the different amino acids. When an mRNA and a tRNA that matches a particular triplet code on the mRNA meet at the ribosome, an amino acid is joined to the growing protein.

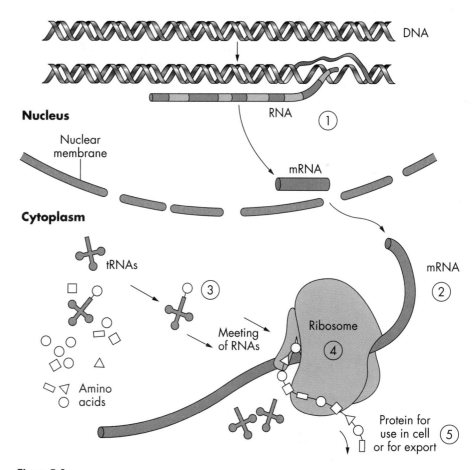

Figure 5.2
1. DNA *produces* mRNA.
2. mRNA *travels* outside the nucleus to the cytoplasm and then attaches to a ribosome.
3. When a tRNA, *picks up* an amino acid floating around the cytoplasm, it travels to a ribosome.
4. On the ribosomes, the mRNA *tells* the tRNAs in what order to line up.
5. The result is a protein—a chain of amino acids whose job is to tell cells how to do their job.

Activity 5-1
Making Protein

Introduction

Where and how are proteins made in your cells? What is the role of DNA? What is the role of RNA? What is the role of the ribosomes? In this activity you write a script and role-play an important cell process to demonstrate the role of DNA in making RNA and the role of RNA in making proteins in your cells.

Materials

Signs, string, rope
Resource (Optional)
Activity Report

Procedure

Step 1 Write an original script or use the script provided in the Resource that describes the steps involved in making a protein.

Step 2 Share your script with the class. Determine which of the scripts will be used for class presentation. Your teacher will provide copies for the players.

Step 3 Create a human cell formed in bone marrow that makes hemoglobin by placing
- a long piece of string or rope in a circle on the floor to represent the cell membrane.
- a shorter piece of string or rope on the floor inside the cell membrane to represent the nucleus.
- several signs labeled "ribosome" on the floor outside the nucleus.

Step 4 Identify players and have them make and display their signs.

Step 5 Players take their positions and rehearse and perform the acts of the script.

Players	Signs
a. Narrator	Narrator
b. DNA	DNA (GGT-CTC-CTC)
c. Messenger RNA (mRNA)	Make Protein
d. Transfer RNA (tRNA) for Proline	Messenger RNA (mRNA)
e. Transfer RNA (tRNA) for Glutamic Acid 1	Transfer RNA (tRNA)/Proline
f. Transfer RNA (tRNA) for Glutamic Acid 2	Transfer RNA (tRNA)/Glutamic Acid 1
g. Amino Acid Proline	Transfer RNA (tRNA)/Glutamic Acid 2
h. Amino Acid Glutamic Acid 1	Amino Acid Proline (reverse side: The)
i. Amino Acid Glutamic Acid 2	Amino Acid Glutamic Acid 1 (reverse side: Protein)
	Amino Acid Glutamic Acid 2 (reverse side: Hemoglobin)
	3 Ribosome (placed in the cell)

Figure 5.3 Players/Signs Table.

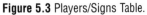

Review Questions

1. What is a protein?

2. What is an amino acid?

3. What is the difference between tRNA and mRNA? Where are they produced and where do they do their work inside the cell?

6

Expressing Dominant and Recessive Genes

Czar Nicholas of Russia, with family.

Why are offspring from the same parents different? How can offspring show traits not seen in either of their parents?

You have learned that each person has two sets of chromosomes, one set inherited from his or her mother and one from his or her father. The chromosomes are made of DNA, and they contain the genes that determine the traits of the individual. So if two sisters each receive half of their chromosomes (with genes) from their father and half from their mother, why are they different? For example, how can one sister have red hair and one sister have brown hair, especially when neither parent has red hair? The answers to these questions are found in the study of classical, or Mendelian, genetics. The word classical refers to the fact that these questions were answered before scientists knew anything about chromosomes, genes, or DNA. The word Mendelian refers to the scientist who first answered these questions a long time ago. You will learn about his famous experiments in this section.

"Every family, aristocratic or not, inherits in their genes a record of who their ancestors were and where they came from."

—*The Language of Genes*
Steve Jones

Long before there was a science of genetics, people did controlled crosses, or breedings, of domesticated plants and animals. It was obvious that specific traits of individual plants or animals could be described, and these traits could be inherited by the offspring of those individual plants or animals. Sometimes a trait of one parent would be expressed in all of its offspring whether or not its mate shared the same trait. Sometimes the traits of the offspring were intermediate between those of the parents, and sometimes the trait of a parent did not show up in its offspring, but reappeared in its grandchildren. All of this underlying information was the special knowledge of plant and animal breeders until the rules underlying the inheritance of traits were discovered by an Austrian monk, Gregor Mendel, in the middle of the 1800s. This was the beginning of the science of genetics.

Gregor Mendel discovered that traits are passed from parents to off-spring as "particles of inheritance" (factors) that we now call genes. For each trait, the offspring inherited one particle from each parent. Some particles of inheritance appeared to be dominant in that they were likely to be expressed in the offspring if they were expressed in either parent. Other particles appeared to be recessive in that they were unlikely to be seen in the offspring if the other parent expressed the dominant trait. For example, if two human parents have blue eyes, their children will have blue eyes. However, if one parent comes from a family line that has always had brown eyes, all of the children will have brown eyes, even though one parent has blue eyes. Brown eye color is a dominant trait. However, sometimes two parents with brown eyes can have a child with blue eyes. Gregor Mendel described rules of particulate inheritance that explain how these patterns of inheritance of traits or **heredity** occur.

The Chromosome Theory of Heredity

Gregor Mendel did not know what a gene was. He did not even know what a chromosome was. He did not know about mitosis and meiosis, either. Right now, you know much more about these things than Gregor Mendel ever did. Mendel guessed that there were things like genes. He then did experiments in which he showed how these particles of inheritance passed from generation to generation. He found out that he could explain the results of his experiments by assuming that each individual inherits two particles (a pair of genes) for each trait, but before reproducing, the individual produced gamete cells that only contained one gene from each pair of genes. This is the process we know of as meiosis. As a result of meiosis, the offspring receives one gene of each of its pairs of genes from its mother and one from its father. However, the gene it receives from its mother could have come through its mother either from its grandmother or its grandfather. The gene it receives from its father could have come from the father's mother or father. This is true for each gene. Thus each offspring receives a unique set of genes. This is why the offspring of the same two parents can be quite different. The

Hypotheses of gene behavior	Observations of chromosome behavior
1. A gamete cell has half the number of genes that a body cell has.	1. Gamete cells have half the number of chromosomes that body cells have.
2. The gene pairs separate during meiosis.	2. Chromosome pairs separate during meiosis.
3. In fertilization, sex cells unite, restoring the original number of genes.	3. In fertilization, sex cells unite, restoring the original number of chromosomes.
4. The individual genes remain unchanged from one generation to the next.	4. Individual chromosomes retain their structure from one generation to the next.
5. The number of possible gene combinations can be calculated.	5. The number of possible chromosome combinations can be calculated.

Figure 6.1 This chart compares gene behavior and chromosome behavior.

Section 6 • Expressing Dominant and Recessive Genes

genes remain unchanged from generation to generation, but they appear in different combinations. Mendel's rules showed how to calculate the probabilities that traits would appear in offspring.

Many years after Mendel, scientists discovered chromosomes and how chromosomes behave in mitosis and meiosis. It was clear that the behavior of chromosomes was very similar to Mendel's hypothesis for how genes had to behave to explain the inheritance of traits. This similarity was strong evidence that genes were found on chromosomes, even though no one had ever seen a gene. Figure 6.1 compares the hypotheses of gene behavior based on Mendel's observations with the observations about how chromosomes behave.

Pedigrees: Tracing Heredity

To understand genetics, it is necessary to do what Mendel did, that is to trace the inheritance of traits through generations. A **pedigree** is one of the tools that geneticists use to study and trace how traits and variations are passed from parents to offspring in a family. A pedigree is a family tree that shows relationships among members of a family. Animal breeders keep pedigrees to trace the characteristics of the animals with which they work. You may have seen a pedigree for a cat, dog, or horse, or you may have seen your own family tree. It is useful for geneticists to create a pedigree for a particular trait. We learned that traits have variations. That means that traits are determined by genes that have slight differences. Different forms of a gene are called **alleles.** A gene pair is made up of a pair of alleles.

There are rules to follow when constructing a pedigree. These rules make it easier for geneticists to understand the pedigrees constructed by other geneticists. Figure 6.2 shows standard symbols used in constructing

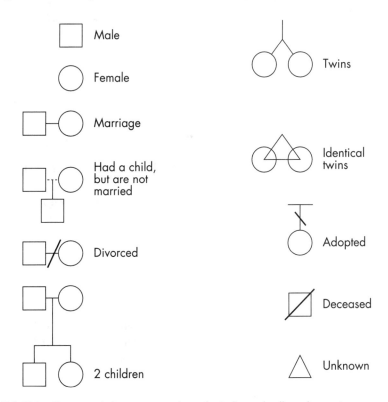

Figure 6.2 Using these symbols, you can make a chart of your family and ancestors.

pedigrees. Members of the same generation are all on the same level. Older generations are on higher levels and younger generations are on lower levels. When placing the offspring of a couple on the pedigree, the oldest offspring is drawn first beginning on the left. Specific alleles can be indicated by shading or coloring the individual symbols.

Pedigrees can help you learn how a trait is inherited. They can help you learn if an allele is a dominant one or recessive one. With this kind of information about a trait, you can predict the probability that it will be expressed in the offspring of a crossing of two individuals. This ability to predict is very important for plant and animal breeders. It is also important for genetic counselors who advise potential parents about the chances their offspring could have a particular genetic disease. In the activity that follows, you look at a pedigree to determine if a particular allele is dominant, and to figure out the rules of inheritance of this trait.

MINI ACTIVITY

Family Pedigree One
Look at the pedigree of a family in Figure 6.3. The variation illustrated on the pedigree is red hair. The symbol for a person with red hair is filled in to show that she or he has the variation being considered. Notice that the pedigree of the family shows four generations. A geneticist needs at least three generations for the pedigree to be useful.

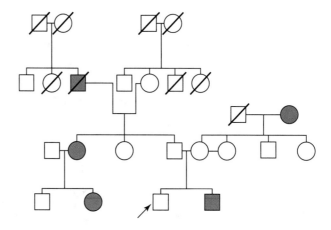

Figure 6.3 This pedigree shows four generations. The shaded circles and squares represent individuals with red hair.

Study the pedigree of the family closely and see what you can learn. Assume this is your family. The arrow points to you.

a. Are you male or female?

b. How many brothers do you have?

c. How many uncles do you have?

d. How many females have red hair?

e. Is red hair due to a dominant or recessive allele?

It is possible to construct pedigrees or family trees like the one above for many different traits. Such pedigrees help to sort out which traits of humans are determined by dominant alleles and which are controlled by recessive alleles. Figure 6.4 lists many traits that are known to be

MINI ACTIVITY

Family Pedigree Two
Draw a pedigree for a man and a woman who are married. They have a son and a daughter. Both the son and the daughter are married. The son and his wife have a son. The daughter and her husband have two children—a daughter and a son. Compare your pedigree with others in your class.

Dominant	Recessive
dark hair	blonde hair
nonred hair	red hair
curly	straight hair
abundant hair	little hair
early baldness	normal hair loss
brown eyes	blue eyes
hazel or green eyes	blue or gray eyes
free ear lobes	attached ear lobes
broad lips	thin lips
large eyes	small eyes
long lashes	short lashes
broad nostrils	narrow nostrils
high, narrow bridge of nose	low broad bridge
Roman nose	straight nose
short stature	tall stature
blood groups A, B, AB	blood group O
tasters of PTC	nontasters of PTC
absence of hair on knuckles	hair on knuckles

Figure 6.4 These are some human traits that are genetically determined and are dominant or recessive.

dominant and many related alleles that are recessive. The construction of pedigrees is a valuable tool for animal and plant breeders. It enables them to keep track of desirable and undesirable traits, determine if they are dominant or recessive, and predict what crosses will favor their expression and which crosses will minimize their expression.

The Genetics of Coat Color in Labrador Retrievers

Imagine that you have a kennel and breed Labrador retrievers. You have bred black Labrador retrievers for years and all of your puppies have always been black. Suppose you have a friend who breeds chocolate Labrador retrievers and her puppies have always been chocolate. The two of you decide to cross your best dogs. The litter of your black female crossed with her chocolate male includes four black males and three black females. The litter of your friend's chocolate female crossed with your black male includes three black males and five black females. Draw the pedigrees for these two crosses. What can you conclude about the dominance of coat-color alleles in Labrador retrievers?

Let's figure out the patterns of inheritance of these alleles. First, you need to know a few more terms and tools that are used by geneticists. For any cross, the parents are designated as the P generation. Their offspring are designated as the F_1 generation. Alleles are labeled with letters. A capital letter means the allele is **dominant.** A lowercase letter means the allele is **recessive.** The genetic makeup of an individual is its **genotype.** The genotype is represented by two letters for each trait, indicating two alleles. Gamete cells are labeled with only one letter because they carry only one allele for the trait.

Now for the pedigrees you constructed for the two crossings of black and chocolate Labrador retrievers, you can write the animal's coat-color genotype into each symbol. Starting with the parents, the black mother and black father would be BB. The chocolate mother and father would be bb. What would the genotypes of the sperm and ova of these dogs be? What would the genotypes of the puppies be? Remember that through meiosis, cells with two alleles for each trait produce gamete cells that have only one allele for each trait. Determine each of the following gamete cell genotypes.

Genotype of gamete cells of the chocolate mother = _____b_____
Genotype of gamete cells of the chocolate father = _____b_____
Genotype of gamete cells of the black mother = _____B_____
Genotype of gamete cells of the black father = _____B_____
Genotype of the puppies of the chocolate mother and the black father cross = _____Bb_____
Genotype of the puppies of the black mother and the chocolate father cross = _____Bb_____

Another way to represent the genetics of a particular cross is to use the allele letters and the symbol for male and female (male = ♂, female = ♀). Then, arrange them in a table that allows you to write down all the possible combinations of the gamete cells of the mother and the father. The square, called a Punnett Square, in Figure 6.6 shows the outcome of a cross between the pure black male and the pure chocolate female.

	Pure black ♂	**Pure chocolate ♀**
Alleles in body cells	BB	bb
Allele in gamete cell	B	b

Figure 6.5 Alleles of a pure black male and a pure chocolate female.

Black ♂ × Chocolate ♀
  BB   bb

Gamete cells of ♀

	b	b
B	Bb	Bb
B	Bb	Bb

Gamete cells of ♂

Figure 6.6 A Punnett Square shows the outcome of a cross between pure black and pure chocolate Labrador retrievers.

This table shows that the genotype of the mother's gamete cells could only be b and the genotype of the father's gamete cells could be only B. Therefore, the genotypes of the puppies could be only Bb. Thus, each puppy would be black, but would carry a recessive allele for chocolate coat color.

You and your friend like your new puppies so much that you decide to keep a few from each litter to breed when they grow up. You keep one male from your friend's litter and one female from your litter to breed. These puppies are the F_1 generation. When they grow up and you breed them to each other, they will create an F_2 generation. Let's see if you can predict what coat colors you will get if you breed your F_1 generation and produce F_2 puppies. We can use the same type of table that is shown above to figure out this problem. First, we have to determine the possible genotypes of the gamete cells of each parent and then the genotypes of the resulting puppies.

In each of the four boxes, combine the allele a puppy would receive from its mother and the one it would receive from its father. Each box will represent a possible genotype for a puppy resulting from this cross. How many will be black? How many will be chocolate?

This set of boxes used to show the possible outcome of a cross is called a Punnett Square. It makes it easy to keep track of all possible combinations of alleles.

Black ♂   ×   Black ♀
  Bb   Bb

Gamete cells of ♀

		B	b
Gamete cells of ♂	B	BB	Bb
	b	Bb	bb

Figure 6.7 A Punnett Square shows the outcome of a cross of the F_1 generation of Labrador retriever puppies.

Try two more crosses. Cross the F_1 genotype with each of the P genotypes. How many black and how many chocolate puppies would you expect from each of these crosses? Your squares only leave room for the four possible genotypes, but what if each litter contained 8 puppies? How many chocolate and how many black puppies would you expect?

If your breeding produce only 4 puppies, how many would you expect would be black and how many would you expect to be chocolate? What is the ratio of black to chocolate puppies? If you did two breedings of your F_1 dogs and produced a total of 16 puppies, how many would you expect to be black and how many to be chocolate?

Activity 6-1
Expression: Dominant and Recessive

Introduction

How is gene expression influenced by dominant and recessive alleles? In this activity you use red and white beans to represent dominant and recessive alleles to simulate allele combinations and gene expression. Then you observe the outcome of these different combinations by recording the resulting physical characteristics of the offspring.

Materials

20 white beans
20 red beans
2 jars or cups
Pen/pencil
Activity Report

Procedure

Step 1   Put 10 white beans and 10 red beans into each of 2 jars representing parents, and mix them up.

Step 2   Without looking, pick a bean from each jar.

Step 3   Record the color of each bean on your Activity Report.

Step 4   Put the beans back into the same jars that they came from, mix the beans, and pick again.

Step 5   Repeat Steps 2 through 4 fifteen times, replacing the beans every time.

Step 6   On your Activity Report, fill in the gene pattern (genotype) column by writing down the allele—red bean = R (dominant) and white bean = r (recessive). For example, if you picked a red bean and a white bean, you would write Rr for the gene pattern.

Step 7   Fill in the column for physical expression or phenotype. The physical expression or phenotype is what the offspring actually looks like. Use the following rules to fill in the column.
• RR is red in color.
• Rr is red in color.
• rR is red in color.
• rr is white in color.

Step 8   Put 10 white beans and 10 red beans into one jar and 20 white beans into the other jar. Repeat Steps 2 through 7. Record your information on your Activity Report.

Step 9   Complete the Activity Report.

Predicting and Explaining Variations

By working on the problems of inheritance of coat color in Labrador retrievers, you have discovered some basic laws of genetics. These laws were discovered over 100 years ago by Gregor Mendel who did similar experiments on pea plants.

Gregor Mendel was the founder of the formal science of genetics. In the 1860s, working with common garden peas, he discovered the basic patterns of inheritance. Mendel was lucky that he decided to work with pea plants, because they have several traits that have only two variations or two alleles. Mendel studied stem length, which has two variations—tall and short; pea pod color—green or yellow; pea seed color—green or yellow; and pea shape—round or wrinkled.

Mendel worked with his pea plants for several years, making sure he had true-breeding varieties. True breeding varieties always produced offspring that were identical to themselves generation after generation. When Mendel mated tall pea plants with tall pea plants and planted those seeds, the plants from those seeds were all tall. When he mated short plants with short plants, the seeds from those plants produced all short plants. Then when he mated a tall plant with a short plant, those seeds all produced plants that were tall. Similarly, when he crossed plants that produced wrinkled seeds with ones that produced round seeds, all of the offspring plants produced round seeds. When he crossed yellow pod plants with green pod plants, all of the offspring had green pods. For each trait Mendel studied, the trait that always showed up (was expressed) among offspring of two different pure breeding plants he called the dominant trait. The trait that did not show up he called the recessive trait.

Mendel did not use the words *gene* or *allele,* but he was able to predict what would happen, and explain what happened when he mated the peas in his garden. He observed that a pair of factors controlled each of the traits he was studying. *Factor* was the word he used. Today we use the words *gene* and *allele.* When a plant had one dominant factor and one recessive factor, the dominant factor was the one that was expressed (observed) in the offspring.

What Do You Think?

The phrase "Every human gene must have an ancestor" is found in the book *The Language of Genes.* What does the phrase mean to you? Write a story or poem about real or imagined ancestors who might have had one or more variations you carry in your DNA today. Be creative. Have fun imagining who these people might have been and what they might have been like.

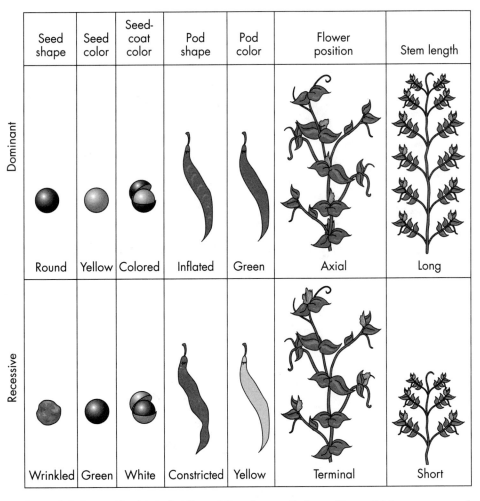

Figure 6.8 Gregor Mendel studied the variations in peas. He learned to predict the appearance of certain characteristics in the offspring, based on whether they were dominant or recessive.

Did You Know?

As geneticists learn more about traits and variations and the genes and alleles that cause them, no one is surprised that there are genes for different traits on the same chromosome. Genes close together on the same chromosome and inherited together are called **linked genes.** The study of linked genes is one of the most exciting things that geneticists concerned with traits and variations in humans are studying today. By studying linkage, geneticists figure out which genes are on which chromosomes, and how close they are to each other on the chromosome. Using these techniques and others, geneticists are making maps of the chromosomes. These maps show where different genes are located.

Gregor Mendel had another important contribution to the study of genetics. He determined that the factors must somehow separate and recombine when the pea plants produced seeds that would become new plants. He knew this because sometimes when plants showing a dominant trait were crossed, some of their offspring showed the recessive trait. This was just like your experiment in crossing the F_1 puppies. When Mendel crossed a tall and a short pea plant and got all tall plants that did not mean the short trait was lost. The short trait was just hidden. Mendel had never seen a chromosome and did not know about meiosis. He did conclude, however, that pairs of factors separate and recombine during the crossing of two plants. What Mendel figured out using the peas in his garden is truly amazing. His discoveries form the foundation for modern genetics.

apply your KNOWLEDGE

Sometimes a baby with blue eyes is born to two parents with brown eyes. Grandparents smile and say "blue eyes skip a generation." Is this myth correct? Can you explain how two brown-eyed parents could have a blue-eyed child?

apply your KNOWLEDGE

- Using Punnett Squares, show the results of crossing a homozygous tall (TT) and a homozygous short (tt) pea plant. Then show the results of back-crossing the F_1 pea plants to each parental type.
- Use the Punnett Square technique to show the results of crossing a tall pea plant with two tall alleles (TT) that has two alleles for wrinkled seeds (rr) with a short pea plant (tt) that has two alleles for round seeds (RR).
- What do you think is the importance of genetic maps?

Review Questions

1. What are alleles? Why are they important?

2. What is the difference between dominant and recessive alleles?

3. Although Gregor Mendel didn't know about meiosis or mitosis, his discoveries provided the foundation for modern genetics. What did he find?

7

Single Gene Disorders

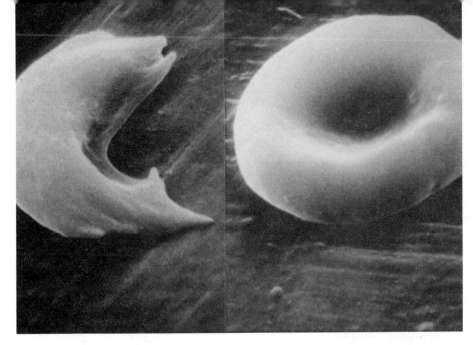

Sickled and normal red blood cells.

What are some genetic conditions that research might be able to help treat or cure?

One reason that geneticists are interested in human traits and variations is because some are recognized as diseases, disorders, or defects. Geneticists, working to control, cure, or prevent these genetic conditions, hope to improve the quality of life.

There are thousands of human genetic conditions caused by single genes. In these conditions, for some reason, the gene does not produce a protein that functions properly. To study these single gene conditions more easily, geneticists have classified them into three groups—dominant, recessive, and sex-linked—based on their pattern of inheritance.

Dominant Inheritance Pattern

In those conditions that have the dominant inheritance pattern, the allele that causes the defect is a dominant allele. In this case, one of the parents has the condition and has the dominant allele. If only one parent has the condition, the children in that family will each have either a 50% or a 100% chance of inheriting it depending on the genotype of the affected parent. If the afflicted parent is **heterozygous,** the children have a 50% chance of receiving the dominant allele and a 50% chance of receiving the recessive allele. Heterozygous means that the person has one dominant allele and one recessive allele. If the parent is **homozygous,** all the children will receive the dominant allele. Homozygous means the person has the same alleles. In this case, the parent has two dominant alleles.

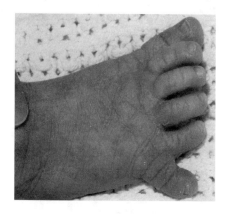

Foot of polydactyl infant.

A homozygous parent for the dominant allele can be represented by DD and a homozygous parent for the recessive allele can be represented by dd. A heterozygous parent can be represented by Dd. Remember that an uppercase letter always stands for the dominant allele and a lowercase letter always stands for the recessive allele. Now use D for the dominant allele and d for the recessive allele to sort alleles according to the possible genotypes of parents. Then you can find out what possible genotypes the different combinations of alleles might produce in their offspring.

There are 1,500 confirmed or suspected dominant abnormal conditions in humans. The names of some of them are
- achondroplasia, which is a form of dwarfism,
- polydactyly, which means having extra fingers or toes, and
- Huntington's disease, which causes progressive dementia later in life.

	h	h
H	Hh	Hh
h	hh	hh

H = gene for Huntington's disease

h = normal gene

Hh = Huntington's disease condition

hh = normal condition

Figure 7.1 In a dominant inheritance pattern, if a heterozygous parent has the allele, there is a 50% chance that any child born will receive the defective gene and have the condition. Also, there is a 50% chance that a child will receive the normal gene and not have the condition.

Recently, the gene for Huntington's disease has been found. A group of researchers in the early 1990s was able to identify the area of the specific chromosome (Chromosome 4) where the gene for Huntington's disease is located by studying a population of affected people in Central America. Huntington's disease is progressive, involving the destruction of brain cells. Usually, death occurs 10 to 20 years after the onset of symptoms. One of the characteristics of Huntington's disease is that affected people usually do not get sick until after they are in their mid-30s. In the future, it may be possible for people to know they will develop the symptoms of a disorder before they actually get the disease, as researchers have been able to do for those with Huntington's disease.

Recessive Inheritance Pattern

Another class of inherited abnormal conditions is recessive conditions. In these conditions, both parents have a single recessive allele for the disorder. Because each of the parents has one recessive allele and one dominant allele, the condition is not apparent in them. It is hidden. Neither parent has the disease, but both are carriers of the disease. There is one chance in four that both parents will pass on the recessive allele to their child resulting in the child having both recessive alleles. The recessive allele will then be expressed and the child will have the disease. If the child received the recessive allele from only one parent, the child would be like the parents, that is, he or she would be a carrier but have no symptoms of the disease. The child could pass the allele on to his or her children.

There is a common mistake that people often make about recessive conditions. Sometimes people mistakenly think that if parents have had one child with a condition, the next child will not have the condition. This conclusion is incorrect. Since each birth is a new event, the chances of having a child with the condition is one in four each time a child is conceived by these parents.

There are over 1,220 confirmed or suspected recessive, abnormal conditions. Some of the common recessive conditions are
- cystic fibrosis, which affects the mucus and sweat glands,
- phenylketonuria, which is a deficiency of an enzyme in the liver,
- sickle-cell disease, which is a disorder of the red blood cells, and
- Tay-Sachs disease, in which the brain is damaged.

Because geneticists are learning much more about recessive disorders, you may read about them in the newspaper or hear about them on television. If you are a good observer, you may see something about a genetic disease almost every day. Have you read anything recently in the newspaper or in a magazine about genetic diseases and some possible new treatments or cures?

Activity 7-1
Exploring a Single Gene Disorder

Introduction
How can a single gene be responsible for causing a genetic condition in humans? What are some examples of single gene disorders? What kinds of treatments are available? In this activity you use models to demonstrate how dominant and recessive alleles interact with each other to cause genetic disorders. Then you select an example of a single gene disorder to investigate.

Materials
2 strips of colored construction paper
2 strips of clear plastic
Activity Report
Computer with Internet connection (Optional)

Procedure
Step 1 Obtain 2 strips of colored construction paper and 2 strips of clear plastic. Place the strips on the table in front of you. Imagine that each strip of paper and plastic is an allele (gene) for the same trait. The colored strips of paper represent

dominant alleles and the clear plastic strips represent recessive alleles.

Step 2 Place a colored strip on top of another colored strip. What do you observe? These alleles contain the same information. The variation represented by this information will be expressed in the individual.

Step 3 Place a colored strip on top of a clear strip of plastic. What do you observe? These alleles contain different information from one another. The variation caused by the dominant allele will be expressed in the individual.

Step 4 Place a clear plastic strip on top of the colored strip. What do you observe? These alleles contain different information from one another. Which variation will be expressed in the individual?

Activity 7-1 (continued)
Exploring a Single Gene Disorder

Step 5 Place one clear plastic strip on top of the other clear plastic strip. What do you observe? In this pair of alleles, the variation caused by the recessive alleles is expressed.

Step 6 Return the strips.

Step 7 Select one of the following single-gene disorders or another one of your choice to investigate. Use the library, local college or university resources, and the Internet, if available, to research the selected single-gene disorder.

- Cystic fibrosis
- Phenylketonuria
- Tay-Sachs
- Polydactyly

What is known about the disorder you selected? On which chromosome is the defective gene located? Are there treatments for this disorder, and, if so, what are they? What do geneticists need to find out in order to treat or cure the disorder?

Step 8 Complete the Activity Report.

X-linked Inheritance Pattern

For some traits, there is a difference in the variations that are expressed (seen) among males and females. For example, many more boys than girls are color-blind. Some of these traits are called **X-linked** or sex-linked. The genes for these traits are part of the X chromosome but are not on the Y chromosome. This is because the X chromosome is larger and possesses more genes.

The Transmission of X-linked Traits

The gene for an X-linked genetic disease is controlled by two alleles. If the expression of the recessive allele results in the genetic disease, then we represent this recessive allele by the lowercase letter n. The normal condition results when the normal allele is present because it is dominant. We represent this allele by the uppercase letter N. The symbols n and N, indicating the X-linked trait are shown on the X chromosome but not the Y chromosome.

Chromosome/ Gene Pattern	Expression
$X^N X^N$	Normal female
$X^N X^n$	Normal female carrying recessive gene
$X^n X^N$	Normal female carrying recessive gene
$X^n X^n$	Female having the genetic disease
$X^n Y$	Male having the genetic disease
$X^N Y$	Normal male

Figure 7.2

A mother carries a defective gene on one of her X-chromosomes. Neither the mother nor the father shows evidence of the genetic disease.

	X^N	X^n
X^N	$X^N X^N$	$X^N X^n$
Y	$X^N Y$	$X^n Y$

Figure 7.3

apply your KNOWLEDGE

Look at Figures 7.2 and 7.3. What are the chances that the daughters of the couple will have the genetic disease? What are the chances that the sons of the couple will have the genetic disease? What proportion of the daughters will carry but not express the genetic disease? Why do more males than females have X-linked genetic diseases?

MINI ACTIVITY

Hemophilia

Hemophilia is an X-linked trait. This is a condition in which the blood fails to clot or clots very slowly after an injury. Like color blindness, hemophilia is caused by a recessive gene. **H** represents normal clotting and **h** represents abnormal clotting. Then $X^h X^h$ and $X^h Y$ would suffer from hemophilia while $X^H X^H$, $X^H X^h$, and $X^H Y$ would be normal. Suppose a nonhemophiliac man marries a nonhemophiliac woman, and they have two children. A son suffers from hemophilia and a daughter is a nonhemophiliac.

1. What is the chromosome/gene pattern of the parents?
2. What is the chromosome/gene pattern of the son and daughter?

The reason X-linked traits are more likely to be seen in males than in females is because the male gets only one X chromosome and the female gets two X chromosomes. Therefore, if a male has a defective gene on his X chromosome, it will be expressed. But if a female has a defective gene on one of her X chromosomes, she still is likely to have a normal allele on her other X chromosome. Remember that a gene codes for a protein. If the X-linked gene is defective in a male, he will have only the defective protein. The female with this gene may also have the defective protein in her cells, but she will have the correct protein as well.

There are over 200 confirmed or suspected X-linked conditions. Some of them are

- red-green color blindness, in which the person cannot distinguish red from green,
- hemophilia, in which blood does not clot properly, and
- some forms of muscular dystrophy, in which the muscles waste away.

You may have heard of hemophilia in your study of history because Alexis, the son of Nicholas II of Russia, had hemophilia. The interference of Rasputin, who promised to cure the disease, is considered by some historians to be one of the causes of the Russian Revolution. More recently, in the 1980s, hemophilia was in the news because some hemophiliacs contracted AIDS from the blood transfusions that they needed then to control their disease. At that time, the blood banks did not have the excellent HIV virus screening procedure that is in use today. Because of these screening techniques for the HIV virus that causes AIDS, the blood supplies in the United States are very safe today.

MINI ACTIVITY

**X-linked Inheritance Pattern—
Color Blindness**
The gene for color blindness is a recessive allele. This allele can be represented by the lowercase letter **c.** Normal color vision is a dominant allele that can be represented by the uppercase letter **C.** X-linked genes are part of the X chromosome but not the Y chromosome. Therefore, the symbols **C** and **c,** representing the color vision trait, are shown on the X chromosome, not on the Y chromosome.

Journal Writing

Imagine that you are completely color-blind. You see a world of black and white all the time. Write a poem about your impressions of the world—a world where color has no meaning but which exists in shades of gray.

The reason that hemophiliacs need blood transfusions is a good example of the fact that genes code for proteins. There are certain proteins that circulate in your blood that can be activated by an injury to a blood vessel. When activated, these proteins cause blood to clot. That clotting stops bleeding from the injured blood vessel. Hemophilia results from a defective gene that cannot make a normal clotting protein. Hemophiliacs used to get that normal protein by transfusions. Many are now able to get the necessary clotting factors or proteins by production in the laboratory through a process called genetic engineering. You will learn more about genetic engineering later in this unit.

Another recessive X-linked trait is color blindness. Look at the table in Figure 7.4. Then answer the following questions about the genetics of color blindness.

1. What will be the chromosome/gene pattern for a color-blind female? What will be the chromosome/gene pattern for a color-blind male?
2. Do more males than females express color blindness? Explain.
3. Two parents who have normal color vision parents produce a color-blind son.
   a. What is the chromosome/gene pattern of the parents?
   b. Can they produce a color-blind daughter? Explain.

Chromosome/ Gene Pattern	Expression
$X^C X^C$	Normal female
$X^C X^c$	Normal female carrying the recessive gene
$X^c X^c$	Color-blind female
$X^C Y$	Normal male
$X^c Y$	Color-blind male

Figure 7.4

Review Questions

1. What is the difference between a dominant inheritance pattern and a recessive inheritance pattern?

2. What is the chance that a son and daughter will be color-blind if their parents are not color-blind, but their mother's father is color-blind?

8

Other Genetic Conditions and Genetic Counseling

Population geneticist at work.

How do chromosomes and the environment contribute to human variation?

In addition to the genetic conditions caused by a single gene, there are other genetic conditions caused by the interaction of several genes that are considered diseases, disorders, or defects.

What Do You Think?

Insurance companies compensate people for medical expenses. Should they be allowed to screen people for genetic disorders before agreeing to insure them?

Conditions Caused by Several Genes

Some genetic conditions resulting in physical abnormalities are caused, not by a single gene, but by the interaction of several genes. Because several genes cause the condition, determining the chance of the condition being passed from a parent to a child is more complicated than for single gene defects. Some of the genetic conditions caused by the interaction of several genes include the following.

- Cleft lip, in which the person is born with a deformed upper lip
- Club foot, a condition in which the foot is turned in

Chromosomal Disorders

Some genetic conditions are caused not by a single gene or the interaction of several genes, but by a chromosomal error. Sometimes chromosomes break during meiosis and a person is born with a piece of chromosome missing. Sometimes, during meiosis, the chromosomes do not separate properly, and a person is born with 47 chromosomes, instead of 46. The best known example of this kind of chromosomal condition is Down syndrome. People with Down syndrome have 3 copies of chromosome 21 instead of only 2 copies. They usually have an extra fold of skin near the eye, a large tongue, and small hands with short fingers. In addition, they may have defects of the heart, eyes, and ears. They also tend to have learning disabilities of various degrees of severity. Just as there is great diversity among people without Down syndrome, there also is great diversity among people who have Down syndrome. Some individuals with Down syndrome can function in society with reasonable independence, while others require a good deal of help and guidance.

Genetic Disease and Environmental Factors

There are a number of common diseases that can be caused by both the environment and the genes you are born with. Cancer and heart disease are two good examples. If you have a parent who had cancer, you are predisposed (more likely) to get cancer yourself. However, these conditions are so closely linked to environmental influences that it is often hard to tell the real cause. For example, suppose a parent dies from lung cancer (abnormal cell growth in the lungs) and smoked most of his or her life. It is hard to determine if that person developed lung cancer because his or her lungs were particularly sensitive to smoking, or if he or she would have developed lung cancer anyway as a result of heredity. Why do some people get lung cancer from smoking, while others do not?

If a parent has a disease, it is important for you to learn about the nature of that disease and the risk factors that might make it more likely that you, too, will get the disease. Risk factors are the activities and lifestyles you choose that make it more or less likely for an outcome to occur. For example, if you choose to be an emergency room physician, you will work in a stressful profession. You may be more likely to develop stress-related problems such as high blood pressure. If your family has a history of heart disease and stroke, a stressful profession might be a risk factor you should minimize. Maybe it would be better for you to become a dermatologist or a pediatrician. Other risk factors for heart disease are smoking, lack of exercise, and a high-fat diet. Everyone should minimize such risk factors. However, it is especially important for those individuals who have a genetic predisposition for developing heart disease to do so.

Genetic Counseling

How do you know if you have a gene that puts you at risk for a disease? **Genetic counseling** is a profession that is mostly concerned with helping people who may have genetic-related conditions. It is estimated that 20% of all people have a genetic condition, have someone in their immediate family (mother, father, brother, sister, aunt, uncle, or cousin) with a genetic condition, or carry the allele for a defect that may be passed onto their children.

Genetic counseling is performed by a team of genetic specialists. This team might include the genetic counselor, a physician, the cytotechnologist (who makes the karyotype), laboratory technicians, and a molecular geneticist who is concerned about the structure and function of DNA. The genetic counselor is the person who coordinates the team and talks directly to the patients.

People see a genetic counselor for one of two reasons. Either they have given birth to a child with a genetic condition or they think they are at risk of giving birth to a child with a genetic condition, because of a family history of the disorder. Families who have given birth to a child with a genetic condition usually ask three questions.

- Why has this happened to us?
- What can we do about it?
- Will it happen again?

People who think they are at risk for giving birth to a child with a genetic condition want to know what that risk is. In both cases, the genetic counselor helps the family learn more about the condition.

What Do You Think?

If you carried a recessive gene for a genetic disorder, and your spouse did too, would you risk having children? Why or why not?

The first thing that a genetic counselor does when working with a family is gather all the information about the traits and variations of the family members to construct a pedigree chart. The genetic counselor will schedule meetings with the geneticist, physicians, and laboratory technicians for the family. The genetic counselor will help the family learn what is known about the condition. The genetic counselor may put the family in contact with other people who have the same genetic condition, so they can provide help and support for one another. There may be a genetic counselor in your community who will come to your class and talk about his or her work.

Population Genetics

In studying genetics, we have considered some of the problems about how traits and variations are passed from parents to children so that there is both continuity and diversity within a species. The first people to study genetics were concerned about the relationship between allele pairs and variations. Molecular geneticists are concerned with problems involving the structure and function of DNA and how it directs the production of proteins in a cell. Genetic counselors are concerned about the health care of families with genetic conditions.

One group of geneticists that we have not discussed are called **population geneticists.** Population geneticists are concerned, not about a single family, but about how and why some alleles are found in people in certain parts of the world and not others. They wonder, for example, why many people in Central Asia have Type B blood, but very few American Indians have this blood type. By studying the genes in a population, population geneticists form a link to those scientists who study evolution. Population geneticists are trying to learn more about how living organisms, including humans, change over time.

Activity 8-1

Investigating the Human Genome Project

Introduction

The Human Genome Project is an international effort to map and sequence all the estimated 80,000 to 100,000 genes in human DNA and to determine and analyze the sequence of the 3 billion (3,000,000,000) chemical bases that make up human DNA. The implications and applications of information gained through this project have already affected human lives. In the next section you will learn more about the Human Genome Project. This activity helps you obtain information about human genes and genetic disorders from the Human Genome Project.

Materials

Human Genome Project address
Computer with an Internet connection
Letter paper, envelope, and stamp
Presentation materials

Procedure

Step 1 Select a number from 1 to 23. This number represents the chromosome you will investigate.

Step 2 Contribute to a class letter to the Human Genome Project Center requesting information about your selected chromosome. In the class letter, request information such as the size of the chromosome, the names and locations on the selected chromosome of the genes identified to date, and what characteristics the identified genes control.

Step 3 When your Human Genome Project information arrives, select one of the genes on your chromosome and investigate the trait (genetic expression) of the gene. If the gene you select has a known disorder, focus your research and presentation on the diagnosis, symptoms, and treatment of the condition.

Step 4 Prepare a presentation to your class about the gene you selected. Your presentation might take the form of a poster presentation, computer presentation, story, or a presentation format of your own choice.

Review Questions

1. What is the difference between a multiple gene disorder and a chromosomal disorder?

2. What are some risk factors for acquiring certain diseases, such as cancer or heart disease?

3. Why is genetic counseling useful?

4. What do population geneticists do?

9

Genetic Engineering

Clone of Dolly and her lamb.

How can learning about DNA solve new problems?

Once scientists recognized the importance of DNA and how DNA controlled the production of proteins, they began to use this knowledge to solve new problems. One problem that scientists had to solve was how to get DNA to make protein in a laboratory. For example, the pancreas of a person who has diabetes may not make insulin. Insulin is a protein that helps the body regulate the use of sugar. Until the 1980s, a person with diabetes had to take artificial insulin that was extracted from the body of a pig. But there were problems associated with using nonhuman insulin. Now human insulin can be made in a laboratory. The production of human insulin resulted from genetic engineering.

The process of getting genes to produce their proteins in the laboratory is called **genetic engineering.** Genetic engineering uses the quick reproducing capabilities of certain types of cells, such as bacterial cells, to make lots of copies of certain proteins, such as insulin. To do this, the genetic engineer must put the DNA gene for the protein to be produced into the bacteria in such a way that the bacteria will duplicate it. The new genetic material in the bacteria is called recombinant DNA (or rDNA).

Bacteria are important workhorses for genetic engineering because scientists can put foreign, recombinant DNA into them. Even though bacteria are simple cells, their own genetic material is very complex. It would be very difficult to put recombinant DNA into the bacterial chromosome. But bacteria can have little circles of DNA outside of their chromosome that replicate like the chromosome replicates. These circles of DNA are called plasmids. Molecular biologists have figured out how to put (or splice) DNA from other organisms into

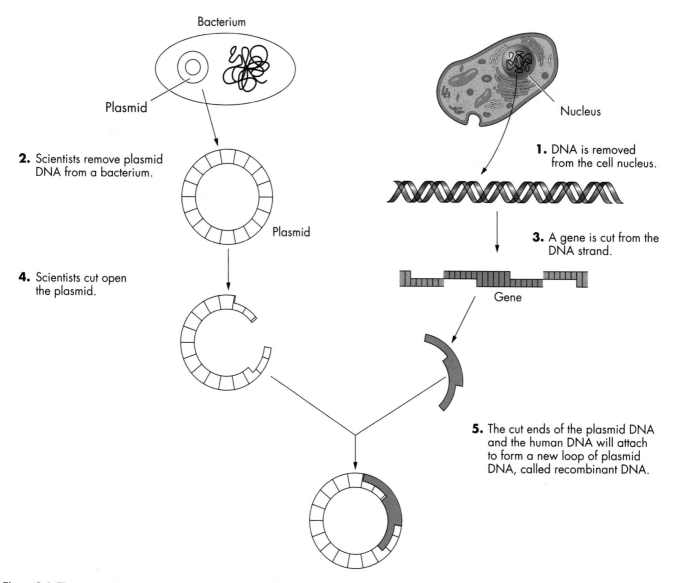

Figure 9.1 The process for making recombinant DNA follows.
1. Scientists remove DNA from a cell nucleus.
2. Scientists remove plasmid DNA from a bacterium.
3. The gene is cut from the DNA strand.
4. Scientists cut open the plasmid.
5. The cut ends of the plasmid DNA and the human DNA will attach to form a new loop of plasmid DNA, called recombinant DNA.

bacterial plasmids. Then the bacteria replicate these plasmids with the inserted genes. In this way, it is possible to use bacteria to make many, many copies of a gene. Making copies of a gene in this way is called **cloning.**

Scientists use special containers that have all the nutrients these bacterial cells need to grow and reproduce as quickly as possible. After the bacterial cells grow and divide many times and produce all of the proteins coded by the plasmid DNA, the scientists open the cells and remove the proteins needed, such as insulin.

The illustration below summarizes how bacteria can be used to make human insulin.

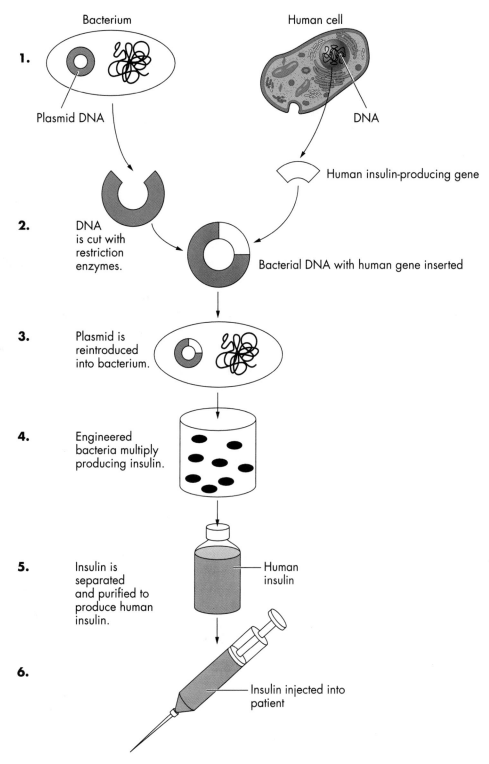

Figure 9.2 The process for making insulin through genetic engineering follows.
1. Scientists remove DNA from a human cell nucleus and plasmid DNA from a bacterial cell.
2. The desired gene is removed from the human DNA and recombined with plasmid DNA.
3. The plasmid is put back into bacteria.
4. Scientists then grow colonies of bacteria in special vessels.
5. Scientists remove the desired proteins from the cells—in this case, insulin.
6. The insulin is purified and, then, is available for human use.

Figure 9.2 makes these processes look simple. However, consider some of the problems that geneticists had to solve to develop this technology to produce insulin. Scientists had to

1. find the human gene that directs the production of insulin,
2. isolate the DNA containing the insulin gene,
3. put (splice) the insulin gene in a plasmid,
4. insert the plasmid into the bacterium,
5. get the plasmid DNA to replicate,
6. get the bacterium to reproduce, and
7. isolate those bacteria that have the plasmid with the human DNA.
8. get the human DNA to function in the bacteria, that is, get the human DNA to replicate and produce the insulin protein.
9. purify the insulin produced.

In spite of all these difficulties, recombinant DNA technology is a rapidly growing area of genetics called molecular genetics. Scientists have reproduced or are close to being able to reproduce the DNA coding for many proteins including the following.

- Insulin, the protein that controls diabetes
- Interferon, a protein that is used in cancer therapy and to prevent and/or cure certain viral diseases such as rabies, hepatitis, and herpes
- Human growth hormone
- An enzyme that breaks up protein
- Cloned anti-viral vaccines are being tested.

Scientists are also using recombinant DNA technology to improve food crops. Imagine a tomato plant that makes a protein that kills the bugs that eat it but is safe for humans. The potential for recombinant DNA technology is unlimited.

Human Genome Project

The Human Genome Project is addressing one of the most monumental problems that scientists are working on—how to locate all of the human genes in the 23 pairs of chromosomes. To solve such a huge problem, geneticists, biologists, chemists, engineers, computer scientists, mathematicians, and many others from all over the world joined together in 1989 to create the Human Genome Project. **Genome** is a word meaning all the DNA-genes of a species. The process of determining the location of a gene on a chromosome is called **gene mapping.** The current estimate is that humans have about 80,000 to 100,000 genes. It also is estimated that there are over 3 billion pairs of nucleotides that make up human DNA.

Some people might ask, "Why would scientists want to be able to locate all of the human genes?" One answer is that scientists, as human beings, are curious about nature. They are always asking *why,* and they want to know more. Another reason to locate all of the human genes is to improve health. There are thousands of genetic conditions that result in

MINI ACTIVITY

Role-Play! Issues in Genetic Engineering
In groups of five, discuss the following question.

Does scientific research, especially in the area of genetics, always serve the best interests of people?

Each person plays one of the following roles.
- Geneticist
- Ordinary person with little knowledge of genetics
- Person with a genetically inherited condition
- Owner of a large drug company that sells proteins such as insulin
- Elected government official, such as a senator

Decide what people's vested interests are. What helps them succeed in their jobs? For example, a geneticist depends on government funding for his or her research laboratory, and receiving that government funding depends on the geneticist's reputation for making new and important scientific discoveries. Or a government official might have many pharmaceutical companies in his or her state.

What Do You Think?

Think of a plant or a genetic condition that might be improved through DNA technology. Write a paragraph describing the improvements you might make. Also discuss some of the risks that might be involved in this genetic engineering project.

an illness or a handicap that are caused by single gene defects. Although some of these conditions have symptoms that can be treated, we have no way to treat the diseases themselves, let alone to cure the people who have the disease. Those working on the Human Genome Project hope that its research will enable us to learn more about genetic diseases and help lead to cures. In addition, those working on the Project believe that the research will provide tools for learning more about the causes of other human diseases including cancer, schizophrenia, and Alzheimer's disease.

The scientists working on the Human Genome Project expect that the entire human genome will be sequenced early in the 21st century. Already the entire genome of some organisms that are simpler than humans have been sequenced. The technology that made it possible to locate, isolate, splice, and clone the gene for insulin is the same technology that is being used in the Human Genome Project.

Exactly 6,218 genes were mapped as of April 19, 1998. Most of the known genes that have been mapped are genes that cause diseases, such as sickle-cell anemia and cystic fibrosis. There is still much work to be done on mapping human genes. But the most important work still remains—figuring out what all of the estimated 80,000 to 100,000 human genes do and how they do it. Also, questions about the variations in human genes need to be addressed. After all, whose genomes are being sequenced by the Human Genome Project? How do they differ from yours?

One important fact about human genes that has been learned is that a gene is not contained in a single continuous location on a chromosome. Rather, a gene seems to have three types of nucleotide sequences. Figure 9.3 shows the three types of nucleotide sequences.

Journal Writing

You are a United States senator arguing about continued funding for the Human Genome Project. Should the project continue to receive funding? If so, should the funding be limited to certain types of research? As a government-funded project, should the project be required to make all of its findings public?

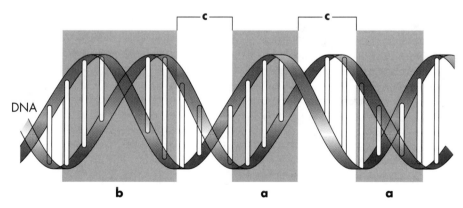

Figure 9.3 Every gene has three types of nucleotide sequences interspersed along a length of DNA. One type of nucleotide sequence is the code for a particular protein **(a)**. Another type of nucleotide sequence, usually at the start of the gene, tells the cell whether or not to make that gene's protein **(b)**. That is, the **(b)** site turns on and turns off the **(a)** site. The last type is nucleotides that don't seem to code for anything **(c)**.

MINI ACTIVITY

Gene Information

Imagine it is the year 2010, and the Human Genome Project has been successful. The names and locations of all of the human genes on chromosomes are known. Discuss the following questions with a group of your classmates.

1. The local hospital is offering free chromosome tests. The tests will take a day and you can learn if you have a genetic predisposition to develop cancer. Will you take the test? Why or why not?

2. You also can find out which other recessive alleles (alleles for traits that are not expressed) you are carrying. Will you take this test? Why or why not?

3. Would you take your children to have these tests? Why or why not? Discuss your responses with the class.

MINI ACTIVITY

Explaining Genetics

Pick one big idea from this unit and design a way to share that idea with someone who is not in your science class. You might choose a parent, since many of the things you studied were not known when your parents went to school. You might choose a younger person in your school or a sibling. Explain the idea with a cartoon, poster, or story.

Some scientists are calling the nucleotides that don't seem to code for anything "junk" DNA. But scientists are learning so much about DNA, we may someday learn that the junk DNA is doing something, maybe even something important.

While the current genetic technology has helped scientists learn quite a lot about human DNA, genes, and chromosomes, it is slow, expensive, and still subject to error. The Human Genome Project itself, however, is improving the quality and precision of genetic technology.

Some people worry that the Human Genome Project will have harmful effects on human life. If we know where all the human genes are located, could parents order a human being with the variations they want, rather than allow the chromosomes with genes and alleles to sort at random (naturally)? Will knowing more about human genes and chromosomes increase tolerance for the great variety of humans or increase discrimination? As a result, one group of people in the Human Genome Project is studying the possible effects the project will have on people so we can avoid and solve potential problems.

Summary

Genetics is the study of the biological causes of genetic continuity and diversity. To learn about continuity and diversity, geneticists study how traits and variations are inherited. Some geneticists study the inheritance of traits and variations at the cellular level. These geneticists are concerned with genes, alleles, and chromosomes. Other geneticists study traits and variations at the molecular level. These geneticists are concerned with the structure and function of DNA and with protein synthesis. Some geneticists are concerned with variations that cause people to be disabled. Other geneticists study inheritance among large groups of people rather than inheritance in individual families.

As a result of their research, geneticists are able to tell us many things about the inheritance of traits and variations. The results of their research also lead to more and more unanswered questions. Genetics is an area of science that is changing very rapidly as we learn more about the human genome. Some geneticists are even studying the ethical and public policy implications of new discoveries in genetics.

MINI ACTIVITY

Concept Map

Review your notes and the key ideas from each section of the text. With a partner, choose 10 concepts that have been presented in the genetics unit. Think like a geneticist and explain how they are related. Use a concept map to display those relationships.

Activity 9-1

Biotechnology in the U.S. Senate

Introduction

Participate in a Senate committee hearing on the future of biotechnology. Here is the scenario.

A molecular biologist has improved ways to clone organisms—plants, animals, and humans. Reactions from your constituents to this technology are mixed and range from support to violent opposition. The question you need to address is, *"Should there be new laws that regulate gene research and genetic engineering?"* You know that science, technology, politics, and ethics, all come together to address this question. What will you recommend to the Senate?

Consider the following issues in determining your response.
- Will this development lead to cures for dreaded diseases such as cancer and AIDS?
- Should there be limits on genetically engineered fruits and vegetables?
- Should there be limits on cloning plants, humans, and other animals?
- How much financial support should the government provide for biotechnology research?

Conduct a Senate hearing to investigate research and applications in the field of biotechnology, specifically, genetic engineering.

Materials

Resources on: genetics; genetic diseases; biotechnology; cloning of plants, humans, and other animals; recombinant DNA technology; gene therapy; costumes and props; and ethical opinions.

Procedure

Step 1 Assign the following roles—senator, expert witnesses such as scientists involved in genetic engineering, members of the public with different opinions on the risks and benefits of genetic engineering, and scientists from companies producing genetically engineered products.

Step 2 Research your assigned role. Become an expert. You are responsible for the information necessary to ask or answer questions. Make up a name and an identity. Dress in appropriate attire.

Step 3 Participate in the Senate hearing that is set up in your class.

Step 4 Submit an opinion paper to the Senate committee at the conclusion of the hearing. The Senate committee will consider your opinions as it prepares its recommendation for the Senate.

 Journal Writing

Do you think the Human Genome Project is more likely to help or hurt humankind? Why? Defend your choice.

 Review Questions

1. What is recombinant DNA? Why is it important?

2. Why are bacteria used in genetic research?

3. What are five necessary steps in making recombinant DNA?

4. Why is mapping human genes important to scientists' knowledge of the human genome?

Glossary

alleles   different forms of genes. A gene pair is made up of a pair of alleles.

amino acids   the building blocks of proteins.

cells   the building blocks of living organisms that perform the functions of the body needed to keep it functioning.

characteristics   the distinctive qualities of living things.

chromosomes   the cell parts that carry the genes.

cloning   making copies of a gene by using bacteria.

continuity   the phenomenon of living organisms producing offspring with similar characteristics.

deoxyribonucleic acid (DNA)   the molecule responsible for the inheritance of traits.

diversity   the variation (or difference) among living organisms.

dominant allele   an allele that is always expressed regardless of whether the other allele of its pair is the same or different.

fertilization   the event of an egg cell, ovum, combining with a sperm cell.

gamete cells   the cells used to reproduce.

gene   a segment or a piece of DNA that codes for a specific trait.

gene mapping   the process of determining the location of a gene on a chromosome.

genetic counseling   a profession that is concerned with helping people who may have genetic-related conditions.

genetic engineering   the process of getting genes to produce their proteins in the laboratory.

genetics   the study of the biological causes of continuity and diversity among living things.

genome   all the DNA genes of a species.

genotype   the genetic makeup for a given individual.

heredity   the process of passing on traits and variations from one generation to the next.

heterozygous   members of a gene pair are different (e.g., Tt).

homozygous   members of a gene pair are the same (e.g., TT or tt).

karyotype   a portrait of the chromosomes of a cell.

linked genes   genes close together on the same chromosome and inherited together.

meiosis   the process that produces gamete cells.

mitosis   cell division in which the nucleus divides, producing two cells each with the same number and exact type of chromosomes as the parent cell.

mRNA   messenger RNA that moves from the nucleus to the cytoplasm carrying the coded message from the DNA in the nucleus to the cytoplasm.

nucleotides   four different complex chemical molecules that make up a DNA molecule. The four complex chemical molecules are adenine, guanine, cyostine, and thymine.

nucleus   the part of a cell that contains the genetic information.

ova   female gamete cells.

pedigree   a family tree that shows relationships among members of a family.

population geneticists   geneticists who are concerned about how and why some alleles are found in people in certain parts of the world and not others.

protein synthesis   the process of making proteins.

recessive allele   an allele that will only be expressed if the other allele of its pair is the same, also recessive.

replication   the duplication of DNA that occurs just before a cell divides.

ribosomes   structures where amino acids are joined together to make a protein.

RNA   a molecule very much like DNA, composed of nucleotides in a single-strand molecule rather than a double-stranded helix.

species   a group of living organisms that has similar characteristics and can interbreed (reproduce among themselves).

sperm   male gamete cells.

trait   a characteristic that can be passed from generation to generation.

tRNA   transfer RNA that carries amino acids to the ribosomes where protein is assembled.

variation   the characteristics that make members of the same species different from one another. Variations are the different forms of a trait.

X-linked   genes for these traits are part of the X chromosome, but are not on the Y chromosome. This is because the X chromosome is larger and possesses more genes.

zygote   a fertilized egg.